The
Rotary Rig
and Its Components

Unit I, Lesson 1
Fourth Edition

By K. R. Bork

Published by

 PETROLEUM EXTENSION SERVICE
Division of Continuing Education
The University of Texas at Austin
Austin, Texas

in cooperation with

 INTERNATIONAL ASSOCIATION
OF DRILLING CONTRACTORS
Houston, Texas

1995

Library of Congress Cataloging-in-Publication Data

Bork, K. R., 1947–
The rotary rig and its components / by K. R. Bork. — 4th ed. p.   cm. —
(Rotary drilling series ; unit I, lesson 1)
"In cooperation with International Association of Drilling Contractors,
Houston, Texas."
ISBN 0-88698-166-2
1. Oil well drilling rigs. 2. Rotary drilling. I. University of Texas at Austin.
Petroleum Extension Service. II. International Association of Drilling
Contractors. III. Title. IV. Series.
TN871.5.B67 1994
622'.3381—dc20

93-49573
CIP

©1995 by The University of Texas at Austin
All rights reserved
First Edition published 1965, Fourth Edition 1995
Third Impression 1997
Printed in the United States of America

Catalog no. 2.10140
ISBN 0-88698-166-2

*No state tax funds were used to publish this book. The University of Texas at Austin
is an equal opportunity employer.*

Contents

▼
▼
▼

Figures

▼
▼
▼

FOREWORD

For many years, the Rotary Drilling Series has oriented new personnel and further assisted experienced hands in the rotary drilling industry. As the industry changes, so must the manuals in this series reflect those changes.

The revisions to both text and illustrations are extensive. In addition, the layout has been "modernized" to make the information easy to get; the study questions have been rewritten; and each major section has been summarized to provide a handy comprehension check for the student.

PETEX wishes to thank industry reviewers—and our readers—for invaluable assistance in the revision of the Rotary Drilling Series. On the PETEX staff, Deborah Caples designed the layout; Doris Dickey proofread innumerable versions; Sheryl Horton saw production through from idea to book; Ron Baker served as content editor for the entire series.

Although every effort was made to ensure accuracy, this manual is intended to be only a training aid; thus, nothing in it should be construed as approval or disapproval of any specific product or practice.

Kathy Bork

Acknowledgments

Special thanks to Ken Fischer, director, Committee Operations, International Association of Drilling Contractors, who reviewed this manual and secured other reviewers, and to Kathy Glass, who kept track of the review process. John Altermann, Reading & Bates Drilling Company; Jim Arnold, Salem Investment; Joey Hopewell, Delta Drilling Company; and Paul Hudson, PETEX-Odessa provided invaluable suggestions on the content and language. Diamond Offshore was extremely generous in allowing us access to an offshore rig—the Ocean America—and two land rigs—rigs 840 and 859. John L. Kennedy graciously gave us permission to adapt drawings from *Fundamentals of Drilling: Technology and Economics* (Tulsa, Okla.: PennWell Publishing, 1983). Jonell Clardy clarified the sometimes difficult text with wonderful new drawings and Terry Gregston braved the weather in the Gulf of Mexico and South Texas to take new photographs.

Units of Measurement

▼
▼
▼

Throughout the world, two systems of measurement dominate: the English system and the metric system. Today, the United States is almost the only country that employs the English system.

The English system uses the pound as the unit of weight, the foot as the unit of length, and the gallon as the unit of capacity. In the English system, for example, 1 foot equals 12 inches, 1 yard equals 36 inches, and 1 mile equals 5,280 feet or 1,760 yards.

The metric system uses the gram as the unit of weight, the metre as the unit of length, and the litre as the unit of capacity. In the metric system, for example, 1 metre equals 10 decimetres, 100 centimetres, or 1,000 millimetres. A kilometre equals 1,000 metres. The metric system, unlike the English system, uses a base of 10; thus, it is easy to convert from one unit to another. To convert from one unit to another in the English system, you must memorize or look up the values.

In the late 1970s, the Eleventh General Conference on Weights and Measures described and adopted the Système International (SI) d'Unités. Conference participants based the SI system on the metric system and designed it as an international standard of measurement.

The *Rotary Drilling Series* gives both English and SI units. And because the SI system employs the British spelling of many of the terms, the book follows those spelling rules as well. The unit of length, for example, is *metre*, not *meter*. (Note, however, that the unit of weight is *gram*, not *gramme*.)

To aid US readers in making and understanding the conversion to the SI system, we include the following table.

Metric Conversion Factors

Quantity or Property	English Units	Multiply English Units By	To Obtain These SI Units
Length, depth, or height	inches (in.)	25.4	millimetres (mm)
		2.54	centimetres (cm)
	feet (ft)	0.3048	metres (m)
	yards (yd)	0.9144	metres (m)
	miles (mi)	1609.344	metres (m)
		1.61	kilometres (km)
Hole and pipe diameters, bit size	inches (in.)	25.4	millimetres (mm)
Drilling rate	feet per hour (ft/h)	0.3048	metres per hour (m/h)
Weight on bit	pounds (lb)	0.445	decanewtons (dN)
Nozzle size	32nds of an inch	0.794	millimetres (mm)
Volume	barrels (bbl)	0.159	cubic metres (m³)
		159	litres (L)
	gallons per stroke (gal/stroke)	0.00379	cubic metres per stroke (m³/stroke)
	ounces (oz)	29.57	millilitres (mL)
	cubic inches (in.³)	16.387	cubic centimetres (cm³)
	cubic feet (ft³)	28.3169	litres (L)
		0.0283	cubic metres (m³)
	quarts (qt)	0.9464	litres (L)
	gallons (gal)	3.7854	litres (L)
	gallons (gal)	0.00379	cubic metres (m³)
Pump output and flow rate	gallons per minute (gpm)	0.00379	cubic metres per minute (m³/min)
	gallons per hour (gph)	0.00379	cubic metres per hour (m³/h)
	barrels per stroke (bbl/stroke)	0.159	cubic metres per stroke (m³/stroke)
	barrels per minute (bbl/min)	0.159	cubic metres per minute (m³/min)
Pressure	pounds per square inch (psi)	6.895	kilopascals (kPa)
		0.006895	megapascals (MPa)
Temperature	°Fahrenheit (°F)	$\dfrac{°F - 32}{1.8}$	°Celsius (°C)
Mud weight	pounds per gallon (ppg)	119.82	kilograms per cubic metre (kg/m³)
	pounds per cubic foot (lb/ft³)	16.0	kilograms per cubic metre (kg/m³)
Mass (weight)	ounces (oz)	28.35	grams (g)
	pounds (lb)	453.59	grams (g)
		0.4536	kilograms (kg)
	tons (tn)	0.9072	tonnes (t)
Pressure gradient	pounds per square inch per foot (psi/ft)	22.621	kilopascals per metre (kPa/m)
Funnel viscosity	seconds per quart (s/qt)	1.057	seconds per litre (s/L)
Power	horsepower (hp)	0.7	kilowatts (kW)
Area	square inches (in.²)	6.45	square centimetres (cm²)
	square feet (ft²)	0.0929	square metres (m²)
	square yards (yd²)	0.8361	square metres (m²)
	square miles (mi²)	2.59	square kilometres (km²)
	acre (ac)	0.40	hectare (ha)
Drilling line wear	ton-miles (tn•mi)	14.317	megajoules (MJ)
		1.459	tonne-kilometres (t•km)
Torque	foot-pounds (ft•lb)	1.3558	newton metres (N•m)

Introduction

Since oil and gas are normally found far below the surface, special means of reaching them and bringing them to the surface must be used. Drilling through perhaps thousands of feet of earth, removing the dirt and rock from the hole as it is drilled, keeping the hole from caving in while it is being drilled, finding a particular layer of earth where oil or gas may be trapped, and providing a means of bringing it to the surface require considerable expertise, labor, and equipment. The primary equipment in this process is the rotary drilling rig and its components.

A rotary drilling rig, whether on land or offshore, may be thought of as a factory designed to produce only one product—an oilwell, or "hole," as it's called in the business. This hole is a carefully planned path from the surface to a formation that may contain hydrocarbons. A rig differs from other manufacturing facilities, however, in that, once the hole is completed and the oil or gas is flowing to the surface, the rig is no longer needed to continue production. Once a well is drilled, the rig and its components can be disassembled, moved, and reassembled at a new location, to begin drilling again.

Portability does not, however, greatly limit a rig's capability to drill, or make hole. It simply makes the rig more cost-effective in that it can be used over and over. Because a rig must be portable, each component can be divided into compact modules and moved overland by trucks, cargo planes, or helicopters, or it can be towed to a new site offshore.

Most rigs are owned by a drilling contractor. Most holes, or wells, are leased by companies engaged in finding, producing, or refining petroleum. These companies are often called operators, or operating companies. An operating company may not be an owner, but a producing company. The company representative represents the operator. The operator hires, or contracts, the drilling contractor to drill the well. The contractor must provide equipment and machinery of sufficient strength and power to drill to the depth the operator specifies.

The drilling crew that operates the rig rotates a bit to drill a well (fig. 1). Weight is placed on the bit so that, as it rotates, its cutters bite into the earth, gouging or scraping the rock away.

Figure 1. A drilling rig rotates a bit to drill a well.

DRILL PIPE

ROTATING BIT

Attached to the bit is a hollow length of pipe. This hollow pipe serves two purposes: (1) it provides the weight to make the bit dig into the formation; and (2) it provides a passageway to circulate a fluid—drilling mud—to the bit as it rotates. This drilling mud cools and lubricates the bit and carries the rock cuttings from the bottom of the hole to the surface (fig. 2). Surface equipment removes the cuttings and a pump recirculates clean mud back down the hole.

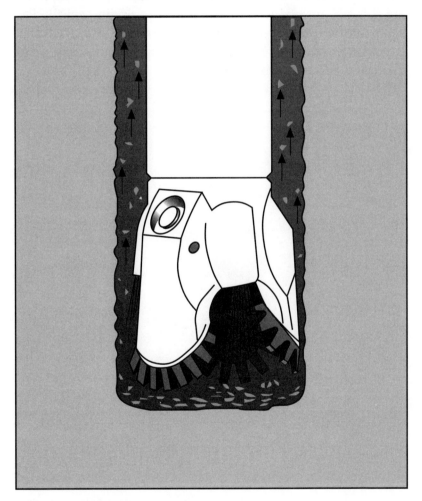

Figure 2. Drilling mud cools and lubricates the bit and carries cuttings to the surface.

As the crew drills deeper, it adds more pipe to that which is connected to the bit. Before a well is completed, this drill stem may be thousands of feet long. During the course of drilling, the drill stem may be pulled out of the hole (tripped) for various reasons, including to change the bit, to run tests on underground formations, or to line the drilled hole with stabilizing pipe (casing) and cement.

The cycle of rotating a bit, adding pipe to lengthen the drill string, lifting it in and out of the hole, and cleaning and recirculating the drilling fluid is the basic process of drilling a well. The equipment needed to perform these functions consists of hoisting, circulating, and rotating components, a derrick or mast to support them, and power to drive them.

Power System

Power is the energy needed to run machinery. On nearly every rig, the power required for drilling the well comes from internal-combustion engines, most often powered by diesel fuel. A rig may need from two to four engines, depending on how deep the well is to be drilled. Big rigs typically have three or four 1,215 horsepower engines with 1,200 kva generators that together may develop 4,860 horsepower, or 3,624 kilowatts.

This horsepower or wattage is transmitted from the engines, or prime movers (the basic source of rig power), to the rig components through two types of drive: mechanical and electrical. On a mechanical rig, belts, chains, sprockets, and pulleys transmit engine power to the parts of the rig. Electric rigs do not require belts, chains, sprockets, or pulleys and transmit electric power from the prime movers to electric motors at each component. Many new medium- to deep-capacity rigs are electric because they are simpler to rig up and maintain than mechanical rigs are.

The power system uses the prime movers and the drives to produce and transmit power for hoisting, circulating, and rotating. (These systems are discussed in later sections.) For detailed information on power systems, see Rotary Drilling Series, Unit 1, Lesson 6: *The Drawworks*, and Lesson 11: *Diesel Engines and Electric Power*.

Introduction

Prime Movers

The prime mover (fig. 3) converts the energy released by the combustion of a fuel into the energy of motion and force. As noted earlier, a rig may need from two to four engines and total rig engine power may range from 500 to more than 4,800 horsepower, or 300 to more than 3,600 kilowatts.

In the early days, when the market for natural gas was extremely limited, it was almost valueless. Thus, it cost little or nothing to use large quantities of it to generate steam for operating a drilling rig. Steam has all but disappeared as a source of power for the operation of rotary drilling rigs, however. Most rigs now use internal-combustion engines as prime movers, and most engines are diesels. Diesel engines produce more torque (twisting force) at low speeds than do gasoline engines. A lot of torque at low speeds is an advantage when driving the large equipment on a rig. Some spark-ignition engines are still in use that burn natural gas or liquefied petroleum gas. Gasoline is not used because the engines burn large quantities of fuel as the well is drilled. Since gasoline is so volatile (i.e., it easily turns into an extremely flammable vapor), it is a very dangerous fuel to store, especially in large amounts.

Figure 3. Prime mover

Whether a rig is on land or offshore, a mechanical or electrical system transmits power from the prime movers to the rig components. Power-delivery systems are called drives.

Drives

On a mechanical-drive rig, the power is transmitted from the engines to the drawworks, the pumps, and other rig machinery through a transmission assembly known as the compound (fig. 4).

Mechanical

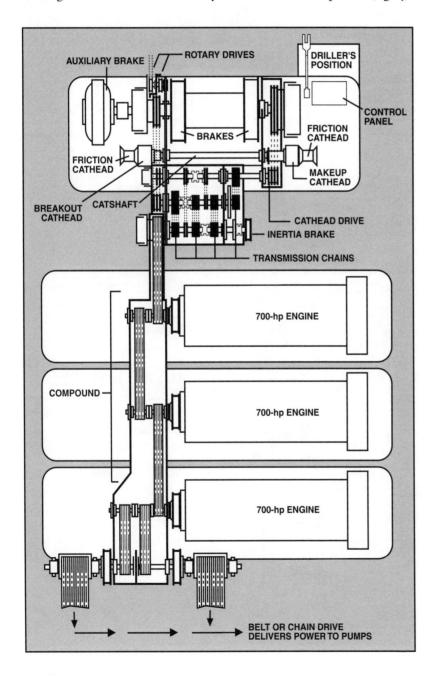

Figure 4. Compound on rig floor

7

The compound consists of clutches, couplings, sprockets, chains, belts, pulleys, and shafts (fig. 5). Two or more engines are compounded, that is, joined, and power is distributed to pumps, drawworks, rotary or top drive, and auxiliaries. Torque-converter drives from the engine to the compound are sometimes used.

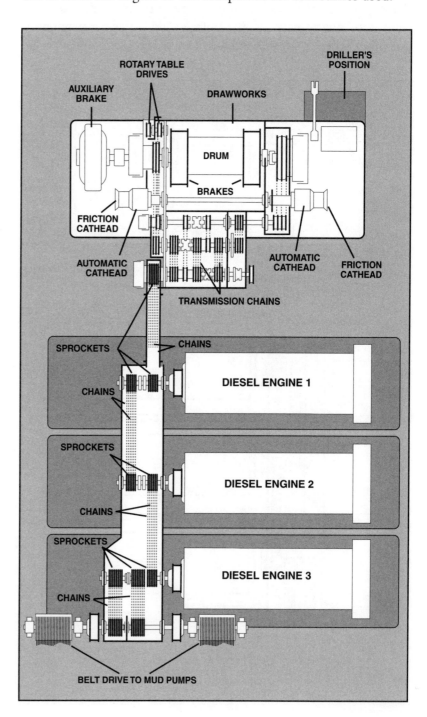

Figure 5. Compound, mechanical rig

On a diesel-electric rig, diesel engines drive large electric genera- *Diesel-Electric*
tors. The generators, in turn, produce electricity that is sent
through cables to electric switch-and-control gear. From here,
electricity goes through additional cables to electric motors that
are attached directly to the equipment involved—drawworks, mud
pumps, and the rotary or top drive (fig. 6).

Today, diesel-electric rigs are replacing the larger mechanical rigs for a number of reasons: (1) they can be rigged up more
quickly and thus are more cost-effective; (2) they operate more
efficiently; (3) they save energy; (4) they allow the higher substruc-
tures required by deeper drilling; and (5) they contribute to noise
abatement because they can be placed well away from the rig floor.
A diesel-electric system also requires less space, so is preferred on
offshore rigs.

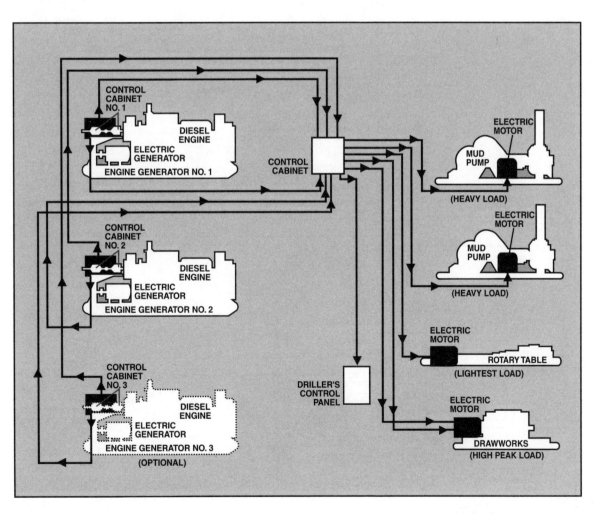

*Figure 6. Diesel-electric
drive*

On a diesel-electric rig, then, the prime movers turn generators that produce easy-to-control-and-transmit alternating current (AC—discussed in the next section). Silicon-controlled rectifiers—SCRs (also discussed in the next section)—convert, or rectify, the AC to direct current (DC), which flows to the motors. Since the motors are powered by DC, it is easy to control their speed (fig. 7).

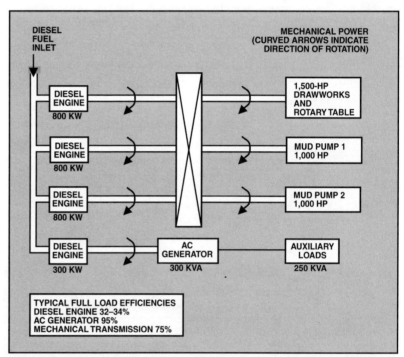

Figure 7. Types of rig power

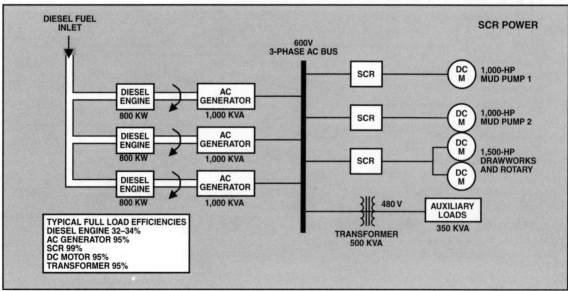

Until the development of the silicon-controlled rectifier in the mid-1960s, most rigs were mechanical; that is, engine power was transmitted to the components by belts, chains, sprockets, and pulleys. The SCR, however, converts AC voltage to DC. (Voltage is electrical force.) The driller varies the speed of the DC motor to operate the drawworks, the rotary or top drive, and the mud pumps.

Alternating current reverses its direction of flow through wires at regularly recurring intervals. It is easy to control and transmit. Direct current flows through wires in only one direction. It, too, is easy to regulate and thus the speed of the motor can be changed easily. A DC motor's main advantage over an AC motor is that it produces a lot of twisting force, or torque, at relatively low voltages.

The layout of a rig's power system is far from standardized. The prime movers, the drawworks, the pumps, and the rotary or top drive may be arranged in any number of ways, depending on the preference of the drilling contractor (fig. 8). Each contractor has different ideas about layout and arranges the rig accordingly.

Variations in layout take power demand into consideration. The hoisting system, when pipe is being raised or casing being run, requires the heaviest power supply. The second biggest user of power is the circulating system. Mud pumps may have their own power source or may be driven from the same engines that drive the rotary or the top drive, which require the least amount of power.

Silicon-controlled Rectifiers

Power System Layout

Figure 8. A possible large land rig layout

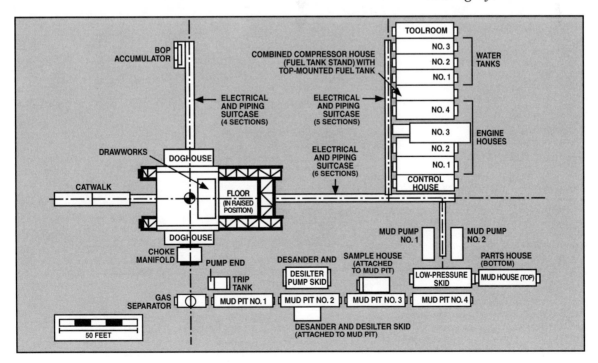

To summarize—

Components of the power system

- Prime mover (usually diesel-powered internal-combustion engines)
- Drive (mechanical or electric)
- Compound (on mechanical-drive rigs)
- Generator (on diesel-electric rigs)

Job of each component

- Prime mover—basic source of rig power
- Drive—transmit power from the prime mover to the rig components
- Compound—distributes power to pumps, drawworks, rotary, and auxiliaries
- Generator—produces electricity that is sent through cables to electric switch and control gear

Hoisting System

▼
▼
▼

Introduction

he hoisting system lifts the drill stem in and out of the hole while drilling a well and lowers the casing into the well. The hoisting system consists of the substructure, the derrick or mast, the drawworks (sometimes called the hoist), the crown block, the traveling block and hook, and the drilling line (or wire rope).

See Rotary Drilling Series, Unit 1, Lesson 5: *The Blocks and Drilling Line*, and Lesson 6: *The Hoist*, for details on this equipment.

The Substructure

The substructure supports the derrick or mast, the rotary table, and the full load of the drill stem when the stem is suspended in the hole or standing in the derrick. It also supports the casing string when the casing is being run in the hole. In addition, its height raises the rig floor high enough to provide space under the rig for large valves called blowout preventers (discussed in a later section). The rig floor holds the drawworks, the driller's control panel, the doghouse, and other equipment.

The Derrick or Mast

A derrick or mast is the steel structure that supports all of the weight of the drill stem or casing, often more than 200 tons (tonnes). A standard derrick has four supporting legs that rest on the steel substructure. It is assembled piece by piece each time a well is drilled. In contrast, a mast is assembled in basic units. After manufacture, it is raised and lowered as a single unit each time a well is drilled. It can, however, be folded, telescoped, or separated into modules to facilitate a move. When a mast is raised and lowered, it looks something like the blade of a huge jackknife being opened and closed. As a result, masts are sometimes referred to as jackknife masts.

The standard derrick—except as found on a few land rigs and most offshore drilling rigs—has become fairly rare, the mast having all but replaced it. A derrick and a mast differ, of course, but in the oil industry, everyone calls a mast a derrick, and this book will follow that convention.

Derrick Load Ratings

Derricks are rated according to the vertical load they can carry and the wind velocity they can withstand from the side. Derrick load-bearing capacity figures may vary from 250,000 to 1,500,000 pounds (111,250 to 667,000 decanewtons) or more. A typical derrick can withstand winds of about 100 to 130 miles (160 to 210 kilometres) per hour with the racks full of pipe and without the need for guy wires attached to ground anchors.

Derrick Height

The derrick and its substructure support the weight of the drill stem at all times, whether the stem is suspended from the crown block (to be discussed in a later section), resting in the rotary table, or standing idle in the derrick. The height of a derrick does not affect its load-bearing capacity, but height does limit the length of the sections of drill stem that the crew can remove from the hole. Derricks are commonly 135 to 145 feet (41 to 44 metres) high. The crown block must be high enough above the derrick floor to permit the withdrawal and temporary storage of the drill stem when it is pulled from the well to change bits or for other reasons.

The Drawworks

The drawworks, sometimes called the hoist (fig. 9), is essentially a large winch that spools off or takes in the drilling line and thus lowers or raises the drill stem and bit. It also raises or lowers the derrick during rig-up and rig-down. Special devices mounted on it (the catheads) screw (make up) or unscrew (break out) threaded pipe connections. It is usually the largest, heaviest, most expensive piece of machinery on a rotary rig.

The drawworks consists of a spool-shaped revolving drum around which wire rope, called the drilling line, is wrapped. When the drawworks is engaged, the drum turns and, depending on the direction it turns, either reels in the drilling line to raise the traveling block (discussed in a later section) or lets out the line to lower it. The drill stem is attached to the traveling block and thus is raised or lowered.

Figure 9. The drawworks

The Catshaft and Catheads

The drawworks also has a catshaft—a kind of axle that crosses through the drawworks. The catshaft is powered and has catheads attached to it. A cathead is used to spin up and tighten the drill pipe joints. One cathead is the makeup cathead on the driller's side of the drawworks (fig. 10). This automatic cathead applies force to a line or a chain. The driller engages it to make up the drill string or when the crew is adding a joint of pipe to the drill string as the hole deepens. A chain runs to the makeup tongs. (Tongs are the large wrenches used to make up or break out drill pipe, casing, tubing, or other pipe—see fig. 11.) A rotary helper latches the tongs around the pipe. When the driller starts the makeup cathead, it spools in the chain. Continued pull by the cathead on the chain makes the tongs tighten the pipe joints.

Figure 10. The makeup cathead

Figure 11. Tongs

17

The breakout cathead is located opposite the driller's position on the drawworks. This automatic cathead looks exactly like the makeup cathead. The driller engages it to take apart, or break out, pipe. Just as the makeup cathead pulls on the makeup tongs to tighten and make up pipe, the breakout cathead pulls on the tongs to loosen and break out pipe.

A spool is attached to each cathead (fig. 12). Fiber rope (catline) can be wrapped around the spool and used to lift and move relatively light loads, such as drill pipe from the catwalk.

Because cathead spools can be deadly if not used with care and common sense, many rigs use an air hoist, or tugger, for handling light loads (fig. 13). These devices use a pneumatically operated motor that, when activated by a rotary helper, reels in or out wire rope attached to the equipment being moved.

Figure 12. Cathead spool

Figure 13. Air hoist

The Brake System   The drawworks brake system enables the driller to control thousands of pounds (or tonnes) of drill pipe or casing. On most rigs, there are at least two brake systems. The main brake is mechanical and can bring the load to a full stop. When it is disengaged, the drawworks drum lets out drilling line to lower the traveling block. The auxiliary brake is hydraulic (e.g., the Hydromatic®—see fig. 14) or electrodynamic (e.g., Elmagco®) and can control the descent speed of a loaded traveling block, although it cannot bring it to a complete halt. The auxiliary brake absorbs some of the momentum a heavy load creates, which allows the main brake to work more efficiently.

Figure 14. Hydraulic auxiliary brake

The drawworks transmission system (fig. 15) gives the driller a wide choice of speeds in hoisting the pipe. The drum on the drawworks may have a minimum of four and often as many as eight speeds.

The Transmission System

Figure 15. Drawworks transmission system

The Blocks and Drilling Line

The crown block, the traveling block, and the drilling line support the load of pipe in the derrick as the pipe is lowered into or withdrawn from the hole. The traveling block is suspended from the crown block by the drilling line (wire rope). During drilling operations, the load the blocks and drilling line must support consists of the hook, the swivel (or top drive), the kelly, the drill pipe, the drill collars, and a bit attached to the bottom of the drill collars. During cementing operations, a string of special pipe called casing has to be lowered into the hole and cemented. Casing is often a heavier load than the drill pipe and collars.

The blocks must be very strong to bear such heavy loads, and as much friction as possible must be eliminated in the blocks. Thus, it is very important that bearings be well made and that the derrickhand lubricate them properly.

For more detailed information on the blocks and drilling line, see Rotary Drilling Series, Unit I: The Rig and Its Maintenance, Lesson 5: *The Blocks and Drilling Line*.

The Crown Block

The crown block is a stationary set of large pulleys, or sheaves (pronounced "shivs") mounted in the top of the derrick (fig. 16). It transfers the weight of the drill string from the drawworks through the drilling line and then to the derrick. Drilling line is threaded, or reeved, through grooves in the sheaves (fig. 17).

Figure 16. The crown block

Figure 17. Drilling line reeved through the crown block

The sheaves around which the drilling line passes are often 5 feet (1.5 metres) or more in diameter, and the pins on which the sheaves rotate may be 1 foot (0.3 metre) or so in diameter.

The Traveling Block

Figure 18. The traveling block

Wire rope (the drilling line) suspends the traveling block from the stationary crown block. Unlike the crown block, however, the traveling block is raised and lowered in the derrick as drilling progresses (fig. 18). Like the crown block, the traveling block also has several sheaves. Attachments to the traveling block include a spring to act as a shock absorber and a large hook to which the equipment for suspending the drill string is attached. The hook on the traveling block can be attached to a cylindrical steel bar called a bail (it is like the handle on a bucket), which supports the swivel or the top drive. Two other bails (often called links) connect the elevators to the hook (fig. 19). Elevators are a set of clamps that rotary helpers latch onto the drill pipe tubulars to allow the driller to raise or to lower the drill string tubulars out of or into the hole. The driller lowers the traveling block and the elevators down to the point at which the floor crew can latch the elevators onto the pipe.

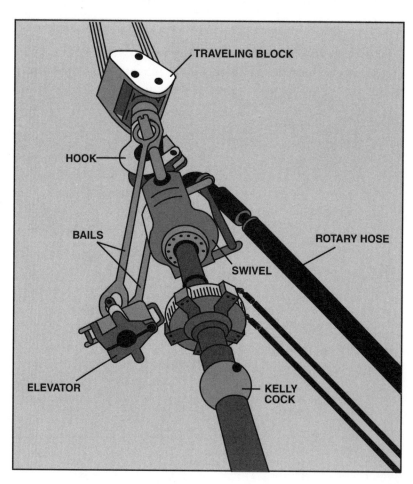

Figure 19. Attachments to the traveling block

Drilling line, often called cable or wire rope, is made by braiding several steel wires (fig. 20). It is especially designed for the heavy loads encountered on a rig.

String-Up

Wire rope (drilling line) may arrive at the rig wrapped on a large supply reel, so it has to be strung up. The drawworks is on the rig floor and the rig's engines are running. The first step in stringing up ("reeving" is the field term) is to take one end of the rope off the supply reel, which is resting on the ground near the substructure, and raise it to the very top of the derrick, where the crown block is installed. The drilling line is reeved (that is, threaded) over a crown block pulley (a sheave) and lowered to the rig floor. The traveling block is tied to the derrick or is resting in a cradle on the rig floor so that it cannot move as the line is reeved through it. The end of the line is reeved through one of the traveling-block sheaves and is raised again to the crown block. There the line is reeved over another sheave in the crown block, lowered again, and reeved through another traveling block sheave. The line is reeved alternately over the crown block and the traveling block until enough lines have been strung to give the drilling line enough lifting strength to support the weight of the drill string.

The number of sheaves needed on the crown block is always one more than the number required in the traveling block. For example, a ten-line string-up requires six sheaves in the crown block and five in the traveling block. The extra sheave in the crown block is needed for reeving the deadline. There is, of course, only one line, but the alternate reeving gives the effect of many lines. The more weight to be supported, the more lines are needed. On a deep hole, workers reeve the line more times, or string more lines, than they do for a shallower hole. Deep wells require more pipe; thus the blocks and line must be able to support heavier loads.

Drilling Line

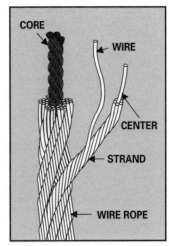

Figure 20. Drilling line

After the workers reeve the line for the last time over the crown block sheaves, they pull the end of the line to the drawworks and secure it to the drum in the drawworks (fig. 21). A worker then powers up the drawworks and takes several wraps of line around the drum, much as an angler reels in fishing line after a cast. Since the traveling block is resting on a support that holds it stationary, the line runs through the block without moving it. The part of the drilling line running from the drawworks to the crown block is the fastline—fast because it moves faster than the other lines in the hoisting system (fig. 21). That is, after the drilling crew readies the rig, the fastline moves on or off the drawworks drum when the driller raises or lowers the traveling block. The relative line speed on each progressive reeve of the line drops until you reach the deadline, which does not move at all.

The end of the line that runs from the crown block to the wire rope supply reel is then secured. This part of the line is called the deadline because, once it is secured, it does not move. Mounted in the rig substructure is a deadline anchor. The deadline is firmly clamped to the deadline anchor (fig. 21). Now the traveling block can be raised off the rig floor and into the derrick by taking in the line with the drawworks. To lower the traveling block, line is let out from the drawworks drum.

Maintenance

Because the drilling line moves constantly through the sheaves of the blocks, it should be inspected frequently to ensure that it is in good condition and has not worn because of the effects of friction. In addition, it should be moved periodically ("slipped" is the field term) so that it wears evenly. Wear is measured in ton-miles (megajoules). When the hoisting line has moved 1 ton (1.02 tonnes) of load over 1 mile (1.6 kilometres), the line has given 1 ton-mile (megajoule) of service.

To slip the line, crew members first hang the traveling block in the derrick so that it cannot move, or they support it on the rig floor in an upright position. In either case, the driller can now pull drilling line through the sheaves without the traveling block's moving. The crew then loosens the clamps on the deadline anchor (fig. 21). The driller starts the drawworks and spools, or slips, the required length of drilling line through the deadline anchor and onto the drawworks drum. Enough line is slipped to ensure that the wear points on the line change. Finally, the crew retightens the deadline anchor clamps, releases the traveling block, and returns to normal operations.

After the driller and the crew slip the line a few times, it could start to accumulate on the drawworks drum. To prevent too much line from collecting on the drum, the crew cuts off excess line at the drawworks end during the slipping operation.

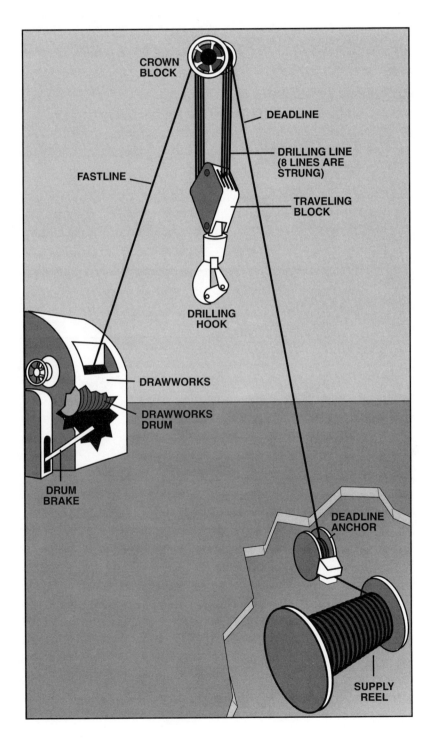

Figure 21. The hoisting system

To summarize—

Components of the hoisting system

- Substructure
- Derrick or mast
- Drawworks (hoist)
- Blocks and drilling line

Job of each component

- Substructure—to support the rig floor, the rotary table, and the suspended drill stem; to provide space for equipment and workers; to provide space under the rig floor for the BOPs
- Derrick or mast—to support the weight of the drill pipe string
- Drawworks—to draw pipe out of and lower it back into the hole
- Blocks and drilling line—to support the load of pipe in the derrick or mast as pipe is lowered into or withdrawn from the hole

Rotating System

▼
▼
▼

The rotating system turns the drill string and the bit to drill a hole. The rotating equipment from top to bottom consists of the swivel or top drive, the kelly, the kelly saver sub, the rotary table, the drill pipe, tool joints, drill collars, and the bit. The assembly of equipment between the swivel and the bit, including the kelly, the drill pipe, and the drill collars (but excluding the rotary table) is the drill stem (fig. 22). Note that in the oil patch "drill string" is often used to mean the drill stem, although, according to the American Petroleum Institute (API), the drill string is simply the drill pipe.

For more information about the rotary, the kelly, and the swivel, see Rotary Drilling Series, Unit 1: The Rig and Its Maintenance, Lesson 4: *Rotary, Kelly, and Swivel.* For more on the drill stem, see Lesson 3: *The Drill Stem*; see Lesson 2: *The Bit*, for details on the bit.

Introduction

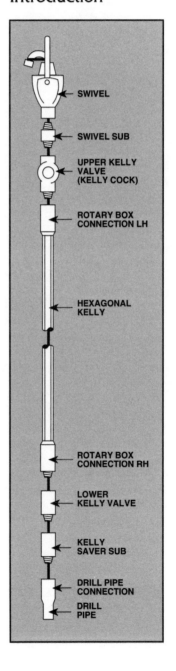

SWIVEL

SWIVEL SUB

UPPER KELLY VALVE (KELLY COCK)

ROTARY BOX CONNECTION LH

HEXAGONAL KELLY

ROTARY BOX CONNECTION RH

LOWER KELLY VALVE

KELLY SAVER SUB

DRILL PIPE CONNECTION

DRILL PIPE

Figure 22. The drill stem

Swivel

A swivel is a remarkable mechanical device (fig. 23) attached to the traveling block by a large bail (handle). It has three main functions: (1) it supports the weight of the drill stem; (2) it allows the drill stem to rotate; and (3) it provides a pressure-tight seal and passageway for the drilling mud to be pumped down the inside of the drill stem. The drilling fluid is under extreme pressure—sometimes exceeding 3,000 pounds per square inch (psi), or 21,000 kilopascals (KPa). It comes in through the gooseneck, a curved, erosion-resistant pipe that connects the swivel to a hose (called the rotary hose) carrying the drilling fluid from the mud pump. It then passes through the washpipe, a vertical tube in the center of the swivel body, and into the kelly and the drill string.

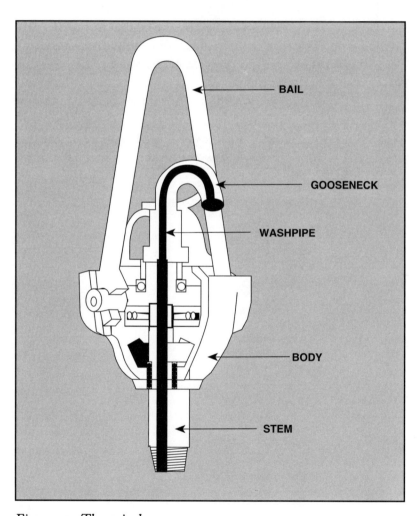

Figure 23. The swivel

Top Drives

Some rigs, especially offshore, use a powered swivel called a top drive (fig. 24) instead of a conventional swivel. The top-drive unit hangs from the traveling block's hook in place of a conventional swivel. The driller raises and lowers the unit as usual, but two vertical rails, firmly attached to the derrick and in which the unit rides, keep the unit from rotating. A heavy-duty motor in the top drive turns a threaded drive shaft. The crew stabs, or inserts, the unit's drive shaft directly into the top of the drill stem. The top drive's motor rotates the drill stem and the bit. During this operation, the rig does not use its kelly, rotary table, master bushing, or kelly drive bushing.

A top drive makes it safer and easier for crew members to handle pipe. With a conventional system, the crew can add only one joint (or length) of drill pipe at a time as the hole deepens, because the kelly must always be in contact with the kelly drive bushing. With a top-drive system, the crew can add pipe three joints at a time, because the top drive has its own power source. A top-drive unit also makes breaking out (unscrewing) or making up (screwing together) pipe safer. The crew uses the unit's built-in tongs (called a pipe handler) to make up and break out pipe directly from the string; no chains or lines run from the drawworks catheads. The top-drive unit's motor provides makeup and breakout power.

Figure 24. A top drive

Kelly

The kelly serves as a passageway for the drilling fluid on its way into the hole and transmits the rotary movement to the drill pipe and bit. It is a four- or six-sided length of pipe. It is not round because its flat sides allow the kelly to turn when the driller lowers it into a square or hexagonal opening in the kelly drive bushing (fig. 25). The kelly drive bushing fits into a master bushing, which, in turn, fits inside the rotary table (fig. 26). As the rotary table turns, the master and kelly drive bushings also turn, causing the kelly to rotate. The drill pipe is connected to the bottom of the kelly, so it, too, rotates.

A standard API kelly is 40 feet (12.2 metres) long. API standards also allow an optional kelly length of 54 feet (16.5 metres), and manufacturers make them in other lengths as well. Since the standard API kelly is 40 feet, most kellys are this length. The longer kelly is used with range 3 drill pipe (43 feet, or 13 metres) and on floating rigs.

Figure 25. The kelly

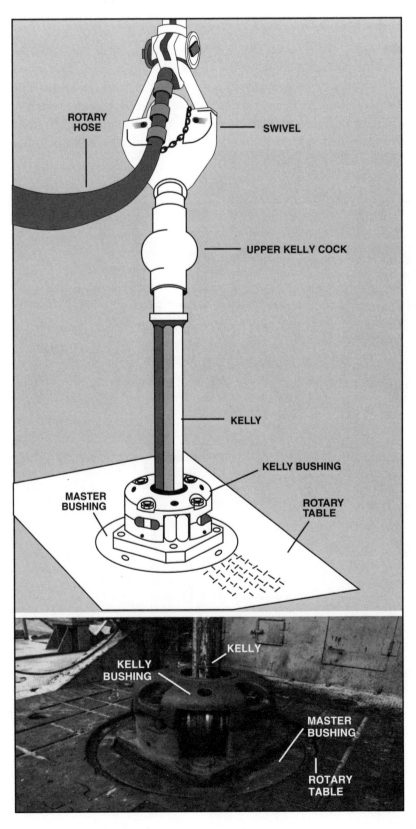

ROTARY
HOSE

SWIVEL

UPPER KELLY COCK

KELLY

KELLY BUSHING

MASTER
BUSHING

ROTARY
TABLE

KELLY

KELLY
BUSHING

MASTER
BUSHING

ROTARY
TABLE

Figure 26. The rotary

33

Kelly Cocks

Upper Kelly Cock

An upper kelly cock (fig. 27) is a special valve that may be recognizable as a bulge on the upper part of the kelly. The upper kelly cock can be closed to shut off rising well pressure from inside the drill stem. Most kelly cocks require a special wrench to operate the closing valve, and the driller should make sure that the kelly cock wrench is kept in one place and that every crew member knows where to find it.

Figure 27. The upper kelly cock

Lower Kelly Cock

A lower kelly cock (also called a lower kelly valve, a drill pipe safety valve, or a drill stem valve) (fig. 28) is usually made up between the lower end of the kelly and the kelly saver sub (fig. 26). When the kelly is high above the rotary table, as it usually is when a joint of pipe is being added to the drill stem (i.e., when a connection is being made), the upper kelly cock cannot be reached easily should it be necessary to close in the drill stem. The lower kelly cock, however, is readily accessible when the kelly is raised.

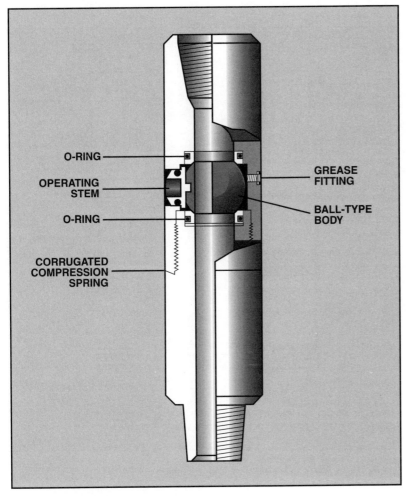

O-RING
OPERATING STEM
O-RING
CORRUGATED COMPRESSION SPRING
GREASE FITTING
BALL-TYPE BODY

Figure 28. The lower kelly cock

Kelly Saver Sub

The kelly's upper end is connected to the upper kelly cock and its lower end is connected to the lower kelly cock. The crew usually installs a special fitting—a kelly saver sub—between the lower kelly cock and the drill pipe. The bottom of the sub (short for substitute) is screwed into the top of each length of drill pipe that is added to the stem (fig. 29). The sub saves wear on the lower kelly cock's threads because, when the sub's threads become worn, the sub—a less expensive piece of equipment—is replaced or rethreaded.

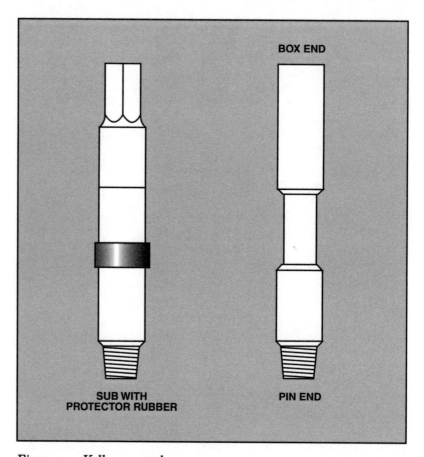

Figure 29. Kelly saver subs

Rotary drilling gets its name from the rotary table (fig. 30). A chain from the compound or an electric motor powers the rotary table. The master bushing fits into the rotary table and drives the kelly bushing (fig. 27). The rotary table also accommodates the slips— a tapered, segmented device lined with strong, toothlike gripping elements (dies) that hold the pipe suspended in the hole when the kelly is disconnected during a trip (fig. 31).

Rotary Table

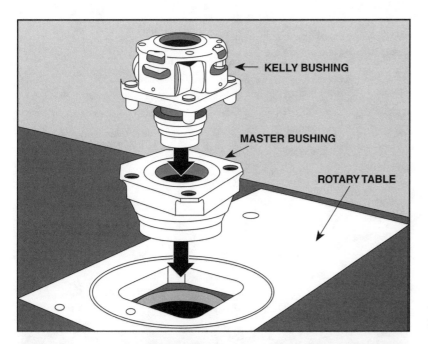

KELLY BUSHING

MASTER BUSHING

ROTARY TABLE

Figure 30. The rotary table

Figure 31. Rotary slips

37

Drill String

The drill string (fig. 32) is made up of the drill pipe and special heavy-walled pipe called drill collars.

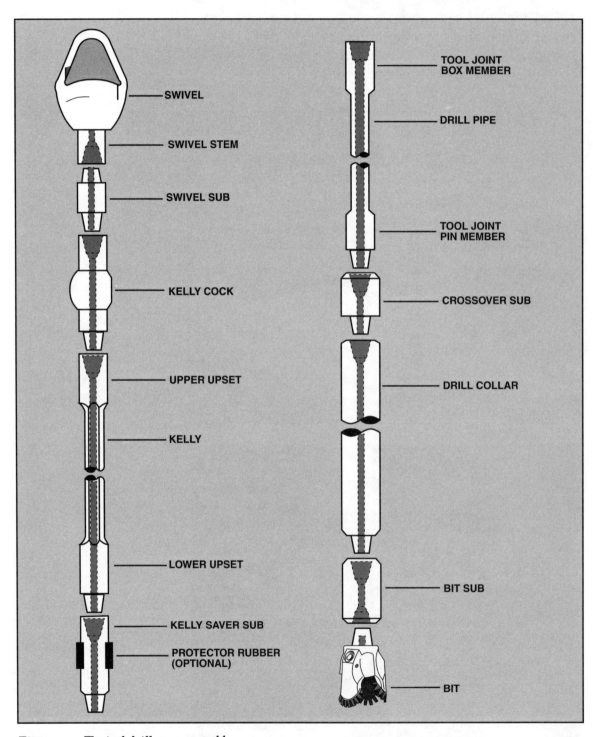

Figure 32. Typical drill stem assembly

Drill pipe (fig. 33) is steel or aluminum tubing used to transmit rotational power and drilling fluid to the bit. A length of drill pipe (without tool joints) may range from 18 to 45 feet (5.5 to 13.7 metres). Range 1 lengths (all but obsolete) vary from 18 to 22 feet (5.5 to 6.7 metres); range 2, from 27 to 30 feet (8.2 to 9.1 metres); and range 3, from 38 to 45 feet (11.6 to 13.7 metres). People usually say that a length of drill pipe is about 30 feet (9.1 metres) long because range 2 pipe is the most commonly used. (With tool joints, range 2 pipe averages slightly more than 31 feet.)

Drill pipe is usually pulled and racked in stands. When a stand consists of three joints of pipe, each about 31 feet (9.4 metres) long (with tool joints), it is sometimes called a thribble. A thribble can be accommodated in a derrick that is 136 feet (41.5 metres) high. Some derricks permit the crew to pull doubles (i.e., two-joint stands) or only singles (i.e., single joints). Offshore, where some drilling units can support taller-than-usual derricks, the crew can pull four-joint stands (fourbles) of range 2 pipe.

See Rotary Drilling Series, Unit 1, Lesson 3: *The Drill Stem*, for more details.

Drill Pipe

Figure 33. Drill pipe and drill collars

DRILL PIPE

DRILL COLLARS

Tool Joints

The threaded ends of the pipe are called tool joints and are actually separate parts that are welded onto the ends of the drill pipe body by the manufacturer. Both ends of each tool joint are threaded. The end of the tool joint with the interior threads is known as the box; the end with the exterior threads is called the pin (fig. 34). When pipe is made up, the pin is stabbed into the box and the connection is tightened.

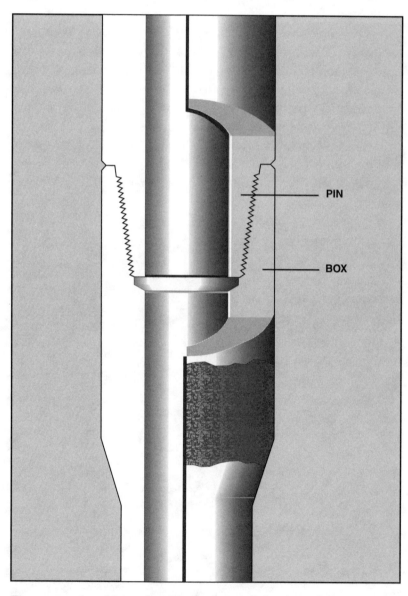

Figure 34. A tool joint showing the box and the pin ends

Drill collars are steel tubes through which mud can be pumped (fig. 35). They are heavier and thicker-walled than drill pipe, however, and are used on the bottom of the string to put weight on the bit. This weight presses down on the bit to get it to drill. Drill collars also maintain weight to keep the relatively flexible drill string from buckling. In combination with the force of gravity, they help maintain the drill stem in a vertical position, which causes the bit to drill a more nearly straight hole. In addition, they help support and stabilize the bit so that it drills new hole aligned with the hole already drilled.

Drill collars are 30 or 31 feet (9.14 or 9.5 metres) long and, unlike the drill pipe, which has tool joints welded on, they have the boxes and pins cut into each end (fig. 35). They weigh from 16 to 379 pounds per foot, or about 24 to 564 kilograms per metre.

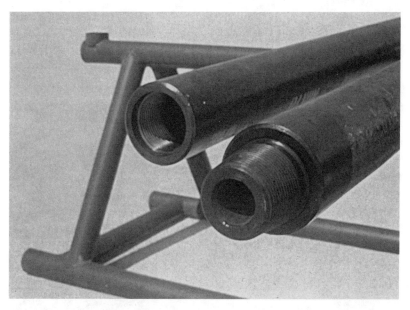

Figure 35. Drill collars

Bits

A bit is attached to the bottom of the drill string and rotated to cut or gouge the formation. Bits range in size from 2 ⅞ inches (75.03 millimetres) to 36 inches (914.4 millimetres) in diameter. Two main types of bits are used for drilling: roller cone and fixed cutter. Fixed cutter bits may be more expensive. Under some drilling conditions, however, they can drill faster and last longer than roller cone bits.

Roller Cone Bits

Figure 36. Roller cone bit

Roller cone, or rock, bits have steel cones, which turn and mesh as the bit rotates. Most roller cone bits have three cones, although some have two and some have four. Bit manufacturers either cut teeth out of the cones (fig. 36), or insert very hard tungsten carbide cutters into the cones. The teeth or cutters gouge or scrape out the formation as the bit rotates. Tungsten carbide bits cost more than steel-tooth bits, but their better performance may offset their higher cost.

All roller cone bits have passages drilled through them to permit drilling fluid to exit. Most bits have nozzles that direct a high-velocity stream, or jet, of drilling fluid to the sides and bottom of each cone so that rock cuttings are swept out of the way as the bit drills (fig. 37). For this reason, oil people sometimes call this type of bit a jet bit.

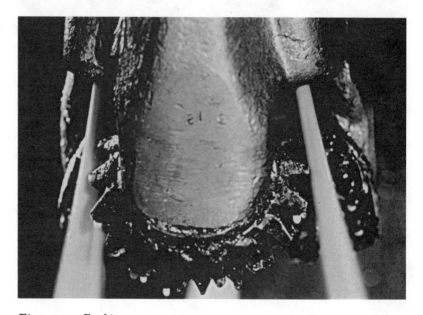

Figure 37. Jet bit

Diamond Bits

Diamond bits do not have cones or teeth. Instead, manufacturers embed industrial diamonds into the bottom and sides of the bit (fig. 38). Since diamonds are so hard, diamond bits are especially suited for drilling hard, abrasive rock formations but can also be used effectively on soft formations.

Figure 38. Diamond bits

Polycrystalline Diamond Compact Bits

The polycrystalline diamond compact (PDC) bit features specially manufactured synthetic diamond cutters, or compacts. The manufacturer sets the PDC cutters in ribs or blades on the bit (fig. 39). These bits shear (or scrape) the formation rather than cut or gouge it; thus less weight is needed on the bit to provide efficient drilling. They are best suited for drilling in shales, clays, and siltstones.

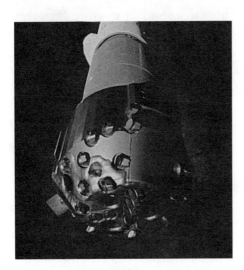

Figure 39. PDC bit

43

Hole Diameter

Crew members usually cannot start at the surface and drill all the way to the final depth in one step. Instead, they begin with a large-diameter bit and drill the hole deep enough to get past loose rocks and dirt that could fall into the hole and create problems, and past water-bearing formations near the surface. Near-surface formations often contain fresh water. Cities sometimes tap these fresh-water reservoirs, or aquifers, to supply their citizens. If the operator failed to protect the aquifers, drilling mud and other fluids could contaminate them.

This first part of the hole is lined with casing and cement, which reduces the hole's diameter and protects those formations near the surface. The depth the crew drills to first may be only a couple of hundred feet or metres or it may be a few thousand feet or metres. It depends on the depth of certain formations that lie relatively close to the surface.

In some cases, the crew can then drill the second part of the hole all the way to final depth. In other cases, however, especially in holes over 10,000 feet (3,000 metres) deep, the crew drills to another predetermined depth, stops drilling, and lines this second part of the hole with casing and cement. Once again, the hole's diameter is reduced by casing and cement, and the third part of the hole will be even smaller in diameter.

Drilling sometimes stops because of so-called troublesome formations. Troublesome formations include those that contain fluids under high pressure or shale formations that break off, or slough (pronounced "sluff") into the hole and impede drilling. Crew members can make adjustments to drill troublesome formations, but these adjustments may not work for the formations that lie even deeper.

In such cases, the crew lines the second, or intermediate, part of the hole with casing and cement before drilling to final depth with a still-smaller bit that fits inside the second casing string. In very deep holes, crew members may have to stop a third time before drilling to final depth.

So, depending on the depth of the well and kind of formations the well penetrates, the well can look like a telescope with only two segments pulled out, or a telescope with three, four, or even more segments (fig. 40). The more segments, or parts, a well has, the larger in diameter the first part of the hole has to be, because each subsequent part will be of a smaller diameter.

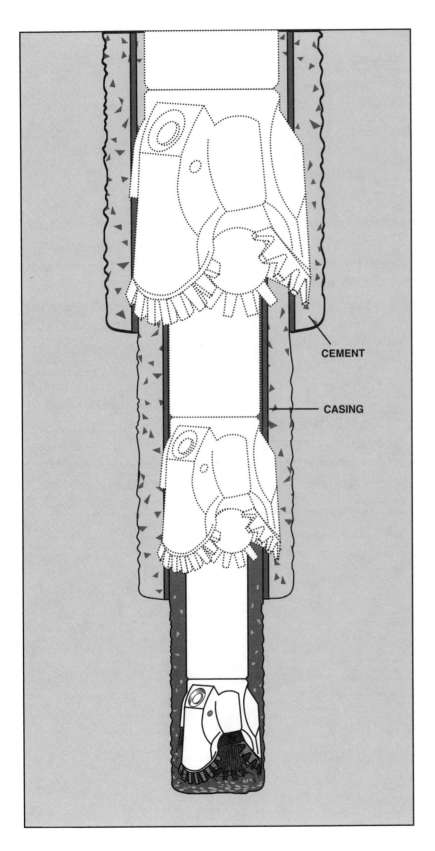

CEMENT

CASING

Figure 40. A hole can look like a telescope with 3 segments pulled out.

To summarize—

Components of the rotating system

- Swivel or top drive
- Kelly
- Rotary table
- Drill string
- Bit

Job of each component

- Swivel—supports the weight of the drill stem; allows the drill stem to rotate; provides a pressure-tight seal and passageway for drilling mud
- Kelly—serves as passageway for drilling mud; transmits rotary movement to the drill pipe and bit
- Rotary table—turns the drill stem and supports the drilling assembly
- Top drive—rotates the drill stem and the bit, eliminating the need for a kelly, a rotary table, a master bushing, or a kelly bushing
- Drill string—the drill pipe and drill collars through which mud is pumped and to which the bit is attached
- Bit—cut or gouge the formation to make a hole

Circulating System

▼
▼
▼

The circulating system (fig. 41) circulates drilling fluid to the bit and back to the surface for cleaning and recirculation. For the rotary drilling system to function, fluid must be circulated downward through the drill stem, around the bit, and upward in the annular space between the drill stem and the wall of the hole or the casing (fig. 42). A circulating system uses the following equipment to circulate, clean, and recirculate drilling fluid: (1) mud pumps; (2) rotary hose; (3) swivel or top drive; (4) drill stem; (5) bit; (6) mud return line; and (7) mud tanks. If the circulating system uses air or gas, compressors must be added.

See Rotary Drilling Series, Unit 1, Lesson 8: *Circulating Systems* for an expanded discussion of the circulating system. Mud pumps are detailed in Lesson 12: *Mud Pumps and Conditioning Equipment*. Auxiliary equipment, such as shale shakers, desilters, and desanders, is discussed in Lesson 9: *The Auxiliaries*, and in a later section of this book.

Introduction

The principal purposes of circulating, or drilling, fluid are to (1) clean the bottom of the hole; (2) cool and lubricate the bit and the drill stem; (3) flush cuttings from the hole; (4) support the walls of the well so that they do not cave in (that is, slough); and (5) prevent the entry of formation fluid into the borehole.

Drilling Fluid

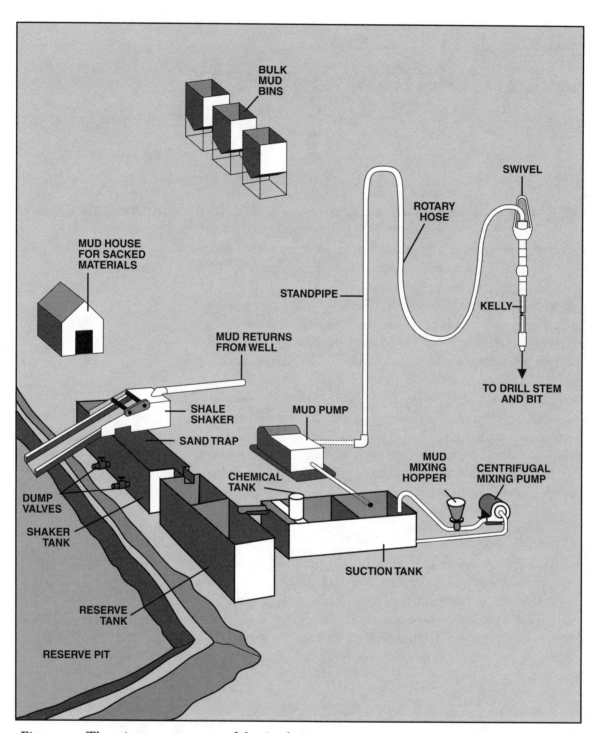

Figure 41. The primary components of the circulating system

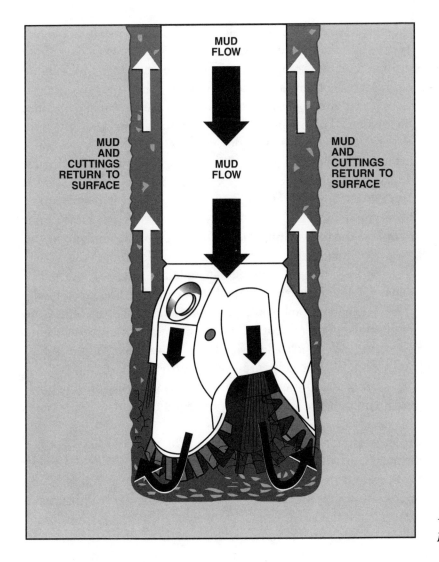

Figure 42. Fluid circulation pattern downhole

The circulating fluid is usually a liquid but can also be air or gas. (A fluid can be either a liquid or a gas.) If the circulating fluid is a liquid, it is composed mostly of water, although occasionally oil (usually diesel fuel) is the major component.

Liquid Muds

49

Both water-base and oil-base drilling fluids are called muds, or drilling muds, because they look like mud. Nevertheless, some drilling muds are complex; special chemical additives and weighting materials are put into them to achieve their purpose. Special clays (most often bentonite or ground attapulgite) make the mud thixotropic. Thixotropic fluid stays liquid as long as it is moving. When a thixotropic fluid stops moving, for example, when the driller stops the mud pump, it gels, or assumes a semisolid state. Thixotropic muds pick up the cuttings made by the bit and lift them up the hole while drilling is going on. When drilling stops, for example, when the crew makes a connection (i.e., adds a joint of pipe to the drill string), and the driller stops the mud pump, the mud gels to keep the cuttings from falling down the hole.

Barite—a heavy mineral—is added to increase the mud's density. Chemicals (such as quebracho, lignite, polymers, modified lignosulfates, and some phosphates) are used to control the mud's thickness, or viscosity, and to improve the ability of the solid particles in the mud to deposit a layer, or wall cake, on the wall of the hole. Wall cake helps prevent the intrusion of formation fluids and controls sloughing. A number of general types of drilling fluids exist, and they are adapted to fit the conditions of a specific well.

Air, Gas, and Foam

If large amounts of formation liquids or high pressures are not expected (the case in perhaps 1 percent of all wells drilled), compressed air, foam, or natural gas is used as the circulating fluid instead of mud. Air, gas, and foam allow very fast drilling. Since these three fluids are so light in weight, or density, they do not develop very much pressure at the bottom of the hole.

The denser a fluid is, the more pressure it develops on bottom. Pressure on bottom tends to hold down the cuttings made by the bit. The cuttings thus get in the way of drilling. As a result, the bit's cutters do not always drill fresh, uncut rock; instead, they redrill cuttings held down by fluid pressure.

Since air, gas, and foam are so light, however, and do not develop much bottomhole pressure, they do not hold down the cuttings. The cuttings immediately get lifted off bottom and the bit drills fresh, uncut formation. Nearly every well contains water, however, so air drilling, although very efficient, cannot be used because the water contacts the fine cuttings produced by air drilling and forms wall cake.

Mud Tanks

The main functions of the mud tanks (often called mud pits) are to (1) accumulate mud circulated from the well; (2) supply fluid to the pump for circulation; (3) store enough mud to provide fluid to fill the hole when pipe is removed, and (4) provide a means of processing (that is, cleaning and treating) the mud.

The mud is mixed in the mud tanks with the help of a mud hopper into which most of the dry ingredients for the mud are poured (see fig. 41). It is very important to note that some dry ingredients, especially caustic, should never be added to the mud through the hopper. The hopper works in such a way that it often throws some of the ingredients being added to it. Since caustic is just that—caustic—a crew member can easily receive a severe burn from such ejected particles. Such dry ingredients should always be added carefully and stirred directly into one of the tanks or into a specially designed caustic barrel. A caustic barrel premixes the powder with water and has a spigot to pour the liquid into the mud tanks. Crew members wear goggles, gloves, and aprons when handling this type of material. The mud tanks contain agitators (paddlelike projections) that mix the mud. The mud is mixed with either oil or water, depending on the mud properties needed.

Mud Pumps

The mud pump is the primary component of any fluid-circulating system. Pump pressure moves the fluid from the pit, through the drill stem, to the bit, back up the annulus, and back to the pit (see fig. 42). Pumps are powered by electric motors attached directly to them or driven by the compound. They may be double-acting two-cylinder (i.e., duplex—fig. 43), or single-acting three-cylinder (triplex) pumps (fig. 44). The pumps for rotary drilling rigs can move large volumes of fluid at very high pressure.

When circulating with air or gas, the pump is replaced by compressors, and mud tanks are not required.

Figure 43. A duplex mud pump

Figure 44. A triplex mud pump

The Mud Cycle

The mud is pumped from the mud suction tank through a discharge line to a standpipe (fig. 41). The standpipe is a steel pipe mounted vertically on one leg of the derrick (fig. 45). The mud is pumped up the standpipe and into a flexible, very strong rubber hose called the rotary, or kelly, hose. The rotary hose is connected to the swivel.

— STANDPIPE

Figure 45. The standpipe

The mud enters the swivel (or the top-drive unit), flows down through the kelly, the drill pipe and drill collars, and exits at the bit. It then does a sharp U-turn and heads back up the hole through the annulus. Finally, the mud leaves the hole through a steel pipe or trough—the mud return line, or flowline—and falls over a vibrating, screenlike device called the shale shaker.

The shaker screens out the cuttings after which they are dispersed. In environmentally sensitive areas (both on land and offshore), the shaker cuttings are collected and treated prior to disposal. The mud drains back into the mud tanks from the shale shaker, is treated, and is recycled back down the hole by the mud pump (fig. 46). The crew member adds water, clay, and other materials to make up for downhole losses and adjusts the mud's properties as the borehole encounters new formations.

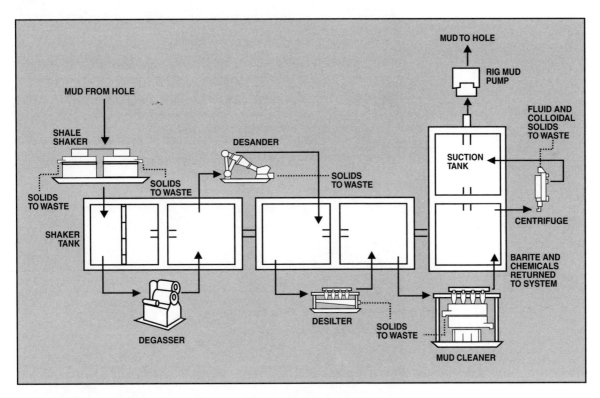

Figure 46. Arrangement of mud tanks and conditioning equipment

Desilters and Desanders

Because fine silt or sand is encountered in most boreholes, desilters (fig. 47) and desanders (fig. 48) are normally mounted on the mud tanks to remove these very small particles. Recirculating silt and sand back down the hole makes the mud heavier and thicker than desired and might erode the drill string and other components.

Figure 47. A desilter

Figure 48. A desander

If a formation containing small amounts of gas is encountered, a degasser is often employed to remove the gas from the mud before it is recirculated into the hole (fig. 49). Mud containing gas (i.e., gas-cut mud) should not be recirculated because it decreases the density of the mud, which could lead to a blowout.

Degassers

Figure 49. A degasser

The science of mud control has developed as rapidly as any phase of the drilling business. It is one of the most complex subjects the drilling crew has to deal with. Variables in any drilling situation not only dictate which chemical and physical makeup of the drilling fluid is best, but also suggest the best circulation rate for the flow of drilling fluid in the hole. In fact, the drilling fluid even has a bearing on the type of bit used and some characteristics of the drilling rig for a given job. For more on mud control, see Rotary Drilling Series 1, Lessons 8 (*Circulating Systems*) and 12 (*Mud Pumps and Conditioning Equipment*).

Mud Control and Hydraulics

To summarize—

Components of the circulating system

- mud pumps
- rotary hose
- swivel or top drive
- drill stem
- bit
- mud return line, or flowline
- mud tanks
- shale shaker

Job of each component

- Mud pumps—circulate the fluid from the pit, through the drill stem, to the bit, back up the annulus, and back to the pit
- Rotary hose—conducts drilling fluid from the mud pump and standpipe to the swivel and kelly
- Swivel—suspends and permits free rotation of the drill stem; provides a connection for the rotary hose and a passageway for the flow of drilling fluid into the drill stem
- Drill stem—provides a conduit for drilling fluid, puts weight on the bit, and turns the bit
- Bit—cuts or bores the hole
- Mud return line—trough or pipe through which drilling mud flows on its return to the pits from the hole
- Mud tanks—accumulate mud circulated from the well; supply fluid to the pump for circulation; store enough mud to provide fluid to fill the hole when pipe is removed; provide a means of processing the mud
- Shale shaker—removes cuttings from the circulating fluid

Well-Control
Equipment

▼
▼
▼

Well-control equipment helps prevent blowouts. A blowout is an uncontrolled flow of gas, oil, or other well fluids into the atmosphere or into an underground formation. It can occur when formation pressure exceeds the pressure applied to it by the column of drilling fluid. A blowout endangers the lives of the crew, can destroy a rig worth millions of dollars, wastes much-needed petroleum, and may damage the environment. Although relatively rare, a blowout is an awesome sight. Fluid (oil, gas, or salt water) erupts from the well, usually with great force, and often ignites into a roaring inferno, especially if the fluid contains gas (fig. 50).

The right amount of drilling mud of the proper density usually prevents the formation fluid from getting into the borehole and blowing out. If the bit drills into a formation with higher-than-expected pressure, however, or if the crew allows the mud level in the hole to drop, formation fluid may enter the hole and the well may kick. During a kick, formation fluid enters the hole and forces some of the drilling mud out of the hole.

Introduction

Figure 50. A blowout

The crew must take corrective actions at the first indication of a kick—when the mud level in the tanks rises and mud flows from the well even when the pump is shut down, or turned off. If the crew delays, all of the mud could spew out of the hole, allowing the formation fluid to flow uncontrolled to the surface. The result is a blowout.

Blowout Preventers

Blowout preventers (BOPs—pronounced "bee-oh-pees"), with other equipment and techniques, are used to close the well in and allow the crew to control a kick before it becomes a blowout. The crew usually installs several blowout preventers (called a stack) on top of the well (fig. 51), with an annular preventer at the top and at least one pipe ram and one blind ram below. This arrangement allows crew members to control an impending blowout, or kick, even if one or more of the preventers fail. Also, some well-control techniques require both the annular and the ram preventers.

Figure 51. A blowout preventer stack

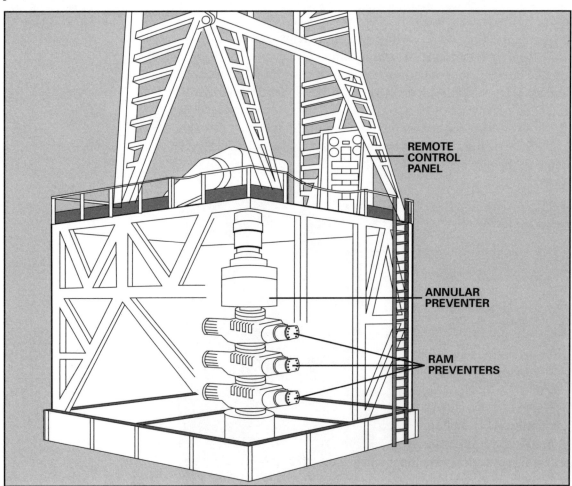

REMOTE
CONTROL
PANEL

ANNULAR
PREVENTER

RAM
PREVENTERS

An annular preventer (fig. 52) has a rubber sealing element that, when activated, seals the annulus between the kelly, the drill pipe, or the drill collars. If no part of the drill stem is in the hole, the annular preventer closes on the open hole. Figure 53 illustrates the annular preventer closing on drill pipe (*A*) and on open hole (*B*).

Annular Preventers

Figure 52. Annular blowout preventers

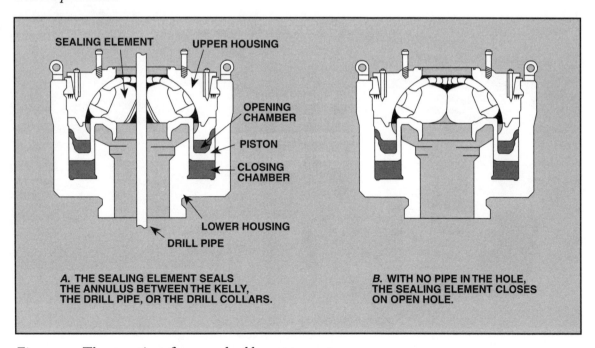

Figure 53. The operation of an annular blowout preventer

Ram Preventers

Ram preventers are large steel valves (the rams) that have sealing elements. One type of ram preventer is called a pipe ram because it closes on the drill pipe; it cannot seal on open hole (fig. 54). Blind ram preventers are straight-edged rams used to close an open hole (fig. 55). Blind-shear rams, used mostly in offshore drilling, cut the drill pipe completely and seal the hole (fig. 56). They allow a mobile offshore unit to move off the location in case of emergency, such as a hurricane. The crew closes the blind-shear rams, which shear the pipe and seal the hole quickly. Since crew members do not have to wait to trip the drill string out, they can move the rig away rapidly. After the emergency is over, the crew can move the rig back to the site, retrieve, or "fish," the sheared string out of the hole, and go back to drilling. This operation—often called cut and run—is a last resort but has saved many mobile rigs from destruction.

Figure 54. A pipe ram blowout preventer

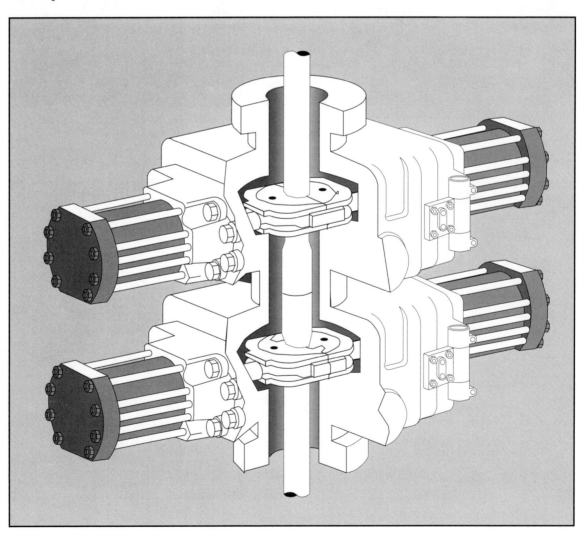

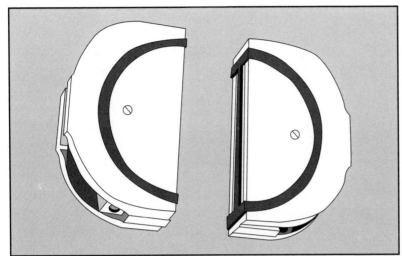

Figure 55. Blind ram preventer

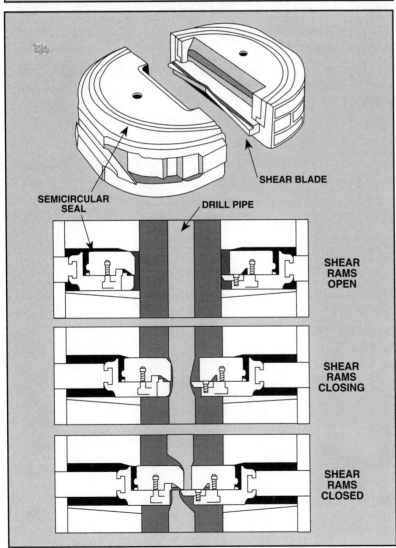

SHEAR BLADE

SEMICIRCULAR
SEAL

DRILL PIPE

SHEAR
RAMS
OPEN

SHEAR
RAMS
CLOSING

SHEAR
RAMS
CLOSED

Figure 56. Blind-shear rams

Accumulators

Blowout preventers are opened and closed by hydraulic fluid, which is stored under pressure in an accumulator (also called a closing unit) (fig. 57). Because the preventers must close quickly, the nitrogen gas in the unit's steel bottles puts the hydraulic fluid under 1,500 to 3,000 pounds of pressure per square inch (about 10,000 to 20,000 kilopascals). High-pressure lines carry the hydraulic fluid from the accumulator to the BOP stack. When the driller operates control valves, the fluid operates the preventers. A remote control panel (fig. 58) located on the rig floor is normally used to operate the preventers.

Figure 57. Accumulator unit

Figure 58. Remote blowout preventer panel

On land locations, the accumulator is usually located at least 50 feet (15 metres) from the rig floor so that, if a blowout and fire occur, the unit is not damaged and can be used to close the preventers. On offshore rigs and on compact land sites, the accumulators are placed as far as practical from the rig floor.

In freezing temperatures, accumulators must be housed properly and heated to allow free flow of hydraulic oil and to keep the electrical controls dry. An antifreeze, such as ethylene glycol, can also be added to the hydraulic fluid.

A choke is simply a valve. There are remote power-adjustable, manual, and fixed (positive) chokes. A power-adjustable choke is operated pneumatically or hydraulically from a remote control panel on the rig floor (fig. 59) and has an opening that is capable of being restricted, or pinched in. It may be infinitely variable in size between full open and closed. A manually adjustable choke has a variable orifice size like the power-adjustable choke but is operated by hand, by turning a handle. A fixed, or positive, choke has a flow restriction of permanent size. In either case, the idea is that the well can be circulated through the choke and adequate back-pressure can be held on the well to prevent the further entry of formation fluids during well-killing procedures.

Chokes

Figure 59. Adjustable choke control panel

Choke Manifolds

When a kick (that is, an influx of formation fluid) occurs, closing in the well with one or more of the blowout preventers is only the first step. To resume drilling, the crew must circulate the kick out of the hole and circulate mud of the proper weight in. Mud of the proper weight balances formation pressure, thereby bringing the well under control, or killing it.

To kill a well, a series of valves called the choke manifold is installed as part of the system (fig. 60). Because chokes can plug and wear under high pressure, several chokes are usually installed. They are arranged to permit switching from one to another, hence the name choke manifold. (A manifold is a series of pipes and valves that can take flow from a single pipe and direct it to several other pipes by means of opening or closing valves.) The choke manifold is connected to the blowout preventer stack with a choke line. When the well is closed in with the blowout preventers, the mud and intruded formation fluid are circulated out the choke line and through the choke manifold.

Figure 60. High-pressure choke manifold

Circulating a Kick

To circulate a kick out of the well and pump heavy mud in, the choke operator opens the choke. At the same time, another person starts the mud pump. As the kick starts moving up the hole, the operator adjusts the size of the choke's opening to hold the proper amount of back-pressure on the well. When the choke operator adjusts the choke correctly, the mud and kick fluids flow out, but no more kick fluids enter the well because the back-pressure held by the choke prevents more formation fluids from entering. The driller and the toolpusher circulate all the kick fluids out and the heavier mud in. They check to ensure that they have the well under control and resume normal operations.

Mud-Gas Separator

A mud-gas separator (fig. 61) saves the usable mud coming out of the well while a kick is being circulated out and separates the flammable gas so it can be burned (or vented) at a safe distance from the rig.

Most mud-gas separators are made of a length of large-diameter pipe. Interior baffles are used to slow the mud-gas stream, and a gooseneck arrangement at the bottom permits the mud to flow to the shaker tank while maintaining a fluid seal in the separator vessel. The gas vent pipe at the top permits the gas to be flared without too much back-pressure on the mud.

Well-control equipment requires that the crew inspect and operate it from time to time to ensure that it is in good operating condition. Frequent blowout drills are common when drilling in areas where formation pressures are expected to be unusually high.

Figure 61. Mud-gas separator

To summarize—

Well-control components

- Drilling mud
- Blowout preventers
- Accumulator (closing unit)
- Choke manifold
- Mud-gas separator

Job of each component

- Drilling mud—prevents formation fluid from getting in the borehole and blowing out
- Blowout preventers—close in the well and allow the crew to control a kick
- Accumulator—stores hydraulic fluid that opens and closes blowout preventers
- Choke manifold—allows mud and intruded formation fluid to circulate out of the well, through the choke line and the choke manifold; maintains back-pressure on the well
- Mud-gas separator—saves the usable mud coming out of the well while a kick is being circulated out and separates the flammable gas so it can be burned at a safe distance from the rig

Auxiliaries

▼
▼
▼

In addition to the major equipment that makes up a drilling rig, many relatively minor pieces of equipment are necessary. The power, hoisting, rotating, circulating, and well-control systems all have support equipment that, added to the major units, makes it possible for the rig to function. The number and type of auxiliaries to be found on a drilling rig are influenced greatly by how the rig is to be used. Such variables as terrain, climate, remoteness from supply centers, and transportation requirements also have to be considered.

For detailed information on the auxiliaries, see Rotary Drilling Series, Unit 1, Lesson 9: *The Auxiliaries*.

Introduction

Modern mechanical rigs are provided with AC generators (fig. 62), nearly always diesel-powered. These engine-generator sets do not provide power for the drawworks, rotary table, and mud pumps. Instead, this AC electricity is used for rig lighting, shale shaker motors, mud pit agitators, centrifugal pumps, rig instruments, engine-cooling fans, and air conditioning for any bunkhouses.

Electric Generators

Figure 62. Engine—AC generator sets

69

Most of these generators have capacities of 50 to 350 kilowatts, although larger units are sometimes installed. In general, the generators can carry the main power load of the rig—excluding hoisting, pumping, and rotating—using only one unit. A second engine-and-generator unit is held in reserve.

Offshore, most rigs are electric. They generate only AC power and distribute it to a common point, or buss. From this point, some AC power is distributed through transformers to the rig's utilities (such as lights) and to small motors (such as those that power centrifugal pumps). The majority of power from the common AC buss is directed through silicon-controlled rectifiers (SCRs), which convert the AC power to DC power. The DC power is then distributed to larger DC motors. In effect, the SCRs convert the AC power to DC power, which is distributed to DC motors that drive the drawworks, the mud pumps, and the rotary table.

Air Compressors

On mechanical rigs (i.e., rigs powered by one or more internal-combustion engines and in which the power is distributed through mechanical devices such as chains, sprockets, clutches, and shafts), a small compressor is usually mounted on the engine compound to supply air for the pneumatic controls and clutches. The compressor has a tank to allow storage of compressed air. Diesel-electric rigs (i.e., rigs powered by diesel engines driving electric generators) usually have an electrically powered compressor to furnish 100 to 150 psi air to pneumatic controls and for other purposes, including starting the main engines and operating the air-powered hoists, air slips, air pumps on the BOP closing unit, water wells, air-operated tools, and the like.

A complete mud system for a heavy-duty compact land drilling rig or almost any offshore rig usually includes 3 tank systems: a shaker tank, where drilled solids and gas are removed; active pits, where the mud is treated back to standard specifications and pumped back down hole; and reserve pits, where treated mud is stored in reserve. The drilling mud first goes to the shale shakers to remove most of the solids. It then drops into the settling pit (also called a sand trap—a 30-barrel, or 4.77-cubic metre, pit). The shaker tank usually consists of 4 to 6 compartments (beginning with the sand trap) where the mud can be processed through various gas- and fine solids–removal equipment in an effort to clean it of unwanted formation contaminants before it is returned to the active pits. The drilling fluid is returned by gravity to an active pit, where weighting materials and chemicals are added to the mud to bring it back up to the standard set by the mud engineer. Finally, it flows into the suction pit from the mud pumps, then back down the hole, where the process is repeated.

Some form of storage for the dry and liquid mud materials is found on most rigs (fig. 63). If a rig is in a remote location, adequate storage for the dry components of the drilling mud is critical so that the mud may be treated readily without waiting for a delivery from the mud company.

Mud Treatment

Figure 63. Mud and chemical storage

Degasser

As mentioned earlier, a degasser (fig. 49) removes small amounts of gas from the mud. Gas may enter the drilling mud as it circulates past a formation that contains gas. The driller cannot recirculate this gas-cut mud back into the hole because the gas makes the mud lighter, or less dense. If the mud gets too light, the well can kick—formation pressure can enter the hole. In rare cases, a kick can lead to a blowout.

Desilters and Desanders

Sometimes the bit creates particles so small that they fall through the shaker. Desilters (fig. 47) and desanders (fig. 48) remove these fine particles, or small solids, to keep them from contaminating the drilling mud.

Drilling Instruments

An instrumentation system is a key part of all rigs. Figure 64 shows the instruments placed at the driller's position for observing drill stem weight, mud-pit level, pump pressure, rotary speed, tong-line pull, and other variables. A mud logging unit, generally supplied by a contracting service company, may be used to keep track of any indications of oil and gas brought up in the circulating fluid.

Other Facilities

Drilling rigs also generally include fuel storage installations; a change house (a place for rig workers to change from work clothes to street clothes); a doghouse (a small structure on the rig floor that serves as an office for the driller and as a storage place for small tools); a toolhouse (a place to store spare parts for the pumps and other equipment); and other facilities. Rigs located in remote areas frequently have a bunkhouse or camp where the crews live while on duty (and other areas frequently offer such a facility as a crew benefit). The toolpusher on most rigs is provided with a trailer that serves as an office, with a telephone, a radio, and a computer for communication with the head office, and as living quarters while on duty.

Offshore rigs are provided with sleeping quarters, food preparation facilities, electric power, water supply, and sewage facilities, as well as storage for enough dry mud, chemicals, cement, oil, and other supplies to operate the rig for many days. And most large rigs can transmit operation data continuously by modem to company headquarters.

Figure 64. Instrumentation system

To summarize—

Auxiliary components and facilities

- Electric generators
- Air compressors
- Mud suction tank, settling tank, reserve pit
- Dry mud storage
- Degasser
- Desilter and desander
- Fuel storage
- Change house
- Doghouse
- Toolhouse
- Bunkhouse or camp
- Toolpusher's trailer

Job of each component

- Electric generators—carry the main power load of the rig, excluding hoisting, pumping, rotating
- Air compressors—supply air for pneumatic controls and clutches; furnish power to start main engines and operate air-powered hoists, air slips, air pumps on the BOP-operating equipment, water wells, air-operated tools, etc.
- Mud suction tank—connected to the mud pump
- Mud reserve pit—stores accumulated surplus mud and cuttings during drilling
- Mud storage—adequate storage for dry and liquid mud materials
- Degasser—removes small amounts of gas from the mud
- Desilter and desander—remove fine particles, or small solids, missed by the desander, to keep them from contaminating the drilling mud
- Change house—where rig workers change from work to street clothes
- Doghouse—office for driller and storage for small tools
- Toolhouse—place to store spare parts for pumps and other equipment
- Bunkhouse or camp—crew quarters
- Toolpusher's trailer—office, communication center, and living quarters

The Crew

Although not actually a rig component, the crew is very important. After all, without crew members, rotary drilling equipment would be worthless.

The drilling crew works for the drilling contractor. Crews may consist of from four to more than six persons. The size of the crew is determined by the type of operation, that is, whether it is on land, on ice-covered tundra, on an inland barge, or on a deepwater offshore rig that may require several specialists not needed on more conventional rigs.

Introduction

The operating company (or operator)—the person or company that actually operates the oilwell or lease—customarily has someone on the drill site to supervise company interests. The operator's supervisor is called the company representative or the company man. This person is in charge of all the operator's activities on the location and lives in a trailer or dwelling on the rig location. The company representative helps plan the strategy for drilling the well, orders needed operator-furnished materials and services, and makes on-site decisions that affect the well's progress. This person and the contractor's toolpusher usually work closely together.

Company Representative

The toolpusher—sometimes called the rig superintendent or the rig manager—is in charge of the rig and overall drilling operations. This crew member directs the actual operation of the drilling rig and the work performed by the drilling crews, authorizes the employment of drillers and crew members, and coordinates interaction between the operating company and the drilling contractor. To keep the rig operating, the toolpusher orders all rig supplies and services that are not supplied by the operating company and is generally on call 24 hours a day. The toolpusher lives in a trailer or portable building on the rig location and has years of experience on a drilling rig as a crew member and driller and expert knowledge of well drilling, rig machinery, tools, and equipment.

Toolpusher

Driller

The driller (fig. 65) is in charge of drilling. This person gives the actual instructions concerning work on the rig to the other crew members and operates the drilling machinery. The driller is under the direct supervision of the toolpusher and is the overall supervisor of the floor workers. The driller and the other members of the crew work 8- or 12-hour shifts, called tours (pronounced "towers").

Figure 65. The driller

Derrickhand

In some countries, the driller has an assistant called a second or an assistant driller who is second in command on the rig floor and relieves the driller at intervals throughout the tour. In the United States, Canada, and other countries, the derrickhand is second in command to the driller and may be thought of as an assistant driller on some rigs. This person works on the monkeyboard, a small platform located up in the derrick at a level even with the upper end of a stand (about 60 or 90 feet [18 or 27 metres]) of drill pipe. When the pipe is being tripped out, the derrickhand handles the upper end of the pipe, guiding it to and from the hoisting equipment used to run pipe in and out of the hole. During drilling, the derrickhand is responsible for maintaining the drilling fluid and maintaining or repairing the pumps and other circulating equipment.

Motorhand and Mechanic

The motorhand is generally responsible for the engines, the engine fuel, and auxiliaries such as the generators, the air compressors, and the water pumps. This person is usually the most experienced rotary helper and checks the lubricating oil and may make minor adjustments to the engines. A mechanic is generally employed for major repairs.

The rig mechanic, if the rig has one (and most land rigs do not), is an all-around fixer when it comes to the mechanical components of the rig. The mechanic may make minor repairs on the engines, small pumps, and various other machinery on or around the rig.

Electrician

The rig electrician maintains and repairs the electrical generating and distribution system on the rig. This person may make minor repairs to generators or electric motors, inspect and maintain the electrical wiring, and maintain the lighting and other electrical appliances. Not all rigs have an electrician.

Rotary Helper

The rotary helper (fig. 66), also known as the roughneck, is responsible for handling the lower end of the drill pipe when it is being tripped in or out of the hole. (Remember: the derrickhand handles the upper end of the pipe during trips.) A full drilling crew can be made up of two to four rotary helpers. They also handle the tongs when making up or breaking out pipe. Besides these duties on the rig floor, rotary helpers often maintain equipment, keep it clean and painted, and keep the rig in good repair.

Figure 66. Rotary helpers

On offshore rigs, contractors have to hire the same type of crew as do contractors on land rigs, but offshore crews include even more personnel. Among the extra personnel are the crane operator and the roustabouts. The roustabouts handle the equipment and supplies that are constantly being supplied to the rig from a shore base. They work under the direction of the crane operator, who maneuvers the crane through the loading and unloading procedures.

Some drilling crews work 8-hour shifts, or tours; others work 12-hour tours. Contractors use 8-hour tours mainly on land rigs drilling relatively close to town because crews can drive to and from the rig to make tour changes.

Drilling goes on 24 hours a day, 7 days a week, all over the world. Rigs may be near a town or city or they may be in a remote area, such as on the North Slope of Alaska or in the jungles of Indonesia. In addition, rigs and righands work more and more in the oceans and seas of the world, as oil and gas that is accessible from land becomes ever more difficult to find. Because of the rig's location, economic factors, and other reasons, the number of days and the number of hours per day that a drilling crew works vary a great deal.

Regardless of the length of their workday, drilling crews call their shifts "tours." In some areas, contractors employ 8-hour tours. In other areas, such as offshore, along the Gulf Coast of Texas and Louisiana, and in remote land locations, they use 12-hour tours.

If the crews work 8-hour tours, the contractor usually hires three drilling crews and one toolpusher for each rig. Three drillers and derrickhands, and six or nine rotary helpers—three full drilling crews—split three tours each day. One crew works the daylight tour from, say, 7:00 AM to 3:00 PM. The second crew works the evening, or afternoon, tour, from 3:00 PM to 11:00 PM. The third crew works the morning tour, from 11:00 PM to 7:00 AM. The toolpusher is always on-site.

Crane Operator and Roustabout

Work Shifts

If the crews work 12-hour tours, the contractor may hire three or four drilling crews and two toolpushers for each rig. One toolpusher, two drillers and derrickhands, and four or six rotary helpers—two full drilling crews—split two tours each day. The two tours may work, say, from midnight to noon and from noon to midnight. With two 12-hour tours, the crews on duty each may work 7 days and then take off 7 days. Other options are the 7-on-and-7-off scheme, the 8-on and 4-off, the 14-on and 7-off, and the 14-and-14 schedule.

Some contractors have rigs working abroad, such as in the North Sea or in Southeast Asia. In such cases, the contractor often institutes a 28-and-28 schedule. Two crews are home for 28 days while the other two work 12-hour tours for 28 days. In some cases, a contractor whose crews work 12-hour tours may hire only three crews to staff the rig. If so, their work schedule is often 8 days on and 4 days off. The three crews work overlapping schedules.

The first 20 days of an 8-and-4 work schedule, 3 crews, A, B, and C, are available. Two crews are on duty while the third is off. In this example, crew A works the 12-hour daylight tour for the first 4 days the rig drills, crew B works the 12-hour night tour, and crew C is off. On day 5, crew A takes off, crew B continues to work at night, and crew C takes over the daylight tour. This alternation continues until the rig finishes the well, which is usually several weeks or months. Note that each crew switches from daylight to nighttime and back after their days off.

	1	2	3	4	5	6	7	8	1	2	3	4	5	6	7	8	1	2	3	4
12-hour daylight tour	A	A	A	A	C	C	C	C	C	C	C	C	B	B	B	B	B	B	B	B
12-hour night tour	B	B	B	B	B	B	B	B	A	A	A	A	A	A	A	A	C	C	C	C
off	C	C	C	C	A	A	A	A	B	B	B	B	C	C	C	C	A	A	A	A

To summarize—

Crew members

- Company representative
- Toolpusher
- Driller
- Derrickhand
- Motorhand
- Mechanic (usually only on offshore rigs)
- Electrician
- Rotary helper (or roughneck)
- Crane operator and roustabout

Job of each crew member

- Company representative—in charge of all the operator's activities on the location
- Toolpusher—in charge of the rig and overall drilling operations
- Driller—in charge of drilling
- Derrickhand—second in command to the driller
- Motorhand—generally responsible for the engines, the engine fuel, and auxiliaries such as the generators, the air compressors, and the water pumps
- Mechanic—all-round fixer of the mechanical components of the rig
- Electrician—maintains and repairs the electrical generating and distribution system on the rig
- Rotary helper—responsible for handling the lower end of the drill pipe when it is being tripped in or out of the hole; handles the tongs when making up or breaking out pipe; maintains equipment, keeps it clean and painted, and keeps the rig in general repair
- Crane operator—maneuvers the crane through the loading and unloading procedures
- Roustabout—handles the equipment and supplies that are constantly being supplied to offshore rigs from a shore base

Work shifts

- 8-hour tours—mainly on land rigs drilling relatively close to town
- 7-on-and-7-off schedule—12-hour tours for 7 days; 7 days off
- 8-on-and-4-off schedule—12-hour tours for 8 days; 4 days off
- 14-and-7 schedule—12-hour tours for 14 days; 7 days off
- 14-and-14 schedule—12-hour tours for 14 days; 14 days off
- 28-and-28 schedule—12-hour tours for 28 days; 28 days off

Glossary

▼
▼
▼

accumulator *n*: 1. a vessel or tank that receives and temporarily stores a liquid used in a continuous process in a gas plant. 2. on a drilling rig, the storage device for nitrogen-pressurized hydraulic fluid, which is used in operating the blowout preventers. See *blowout preventer control unit*.

A

adjustable choke *n*: a choke in which the position of a conical needle, sleeve, or plate may be changed with respect to their seat to vary the rate of flow; may be manual or hydraulic. See *choke*.

A-frame *n*: 1. a derrick or crane shaped like the letter A and used to handle heavy loads. 2. an A-shaped openwork structure that is the stationary and supporting component of the mast of a jackknife rig and to which the mast is anchored when it is in an upright or drilling position. 3. the uppermost section of a standard derrick, shaped like the letter A and used as a support in lifting objects such as the crown block to the water table.

agitator *n*: a motor-driven paddle or blade used to keep the liquid and solid additives in suspension in the drilling mud.

air drilling *n*: a method of rotary drilling that uses compressed air as the circulation medium. The conventional method of removing cuttings from the wellbore is to use a flow of water or drilling mud. Compressed air removes the cuttings with equal or greater efficiency. The rate of penetration is usually increased considerably when air drilling is used; however, a principal problem in air drilling is the penetration of formations containing water, since the entry of water into the system reduces the ability of the air to remove the cuttings.

air hoist *n*: a hoist operated by compressed air; a pneumatic hoist. Air hoists are often mounted on the rig floor and are used to lift joints of pipe and other heavy objects.

alternating current (AC) *n*: current in which the charge-flow periodically reverses and whose average value is zero. Compare *direct current*.

annular blowout preventer *n*: a large valve, usually installed above the ram preventers, that forms a seal in the annular space between the pipe and the wellbore or, if no pipe is present, in the wellbore itself. It can also seal on tool joints, drill collars, or the kelly. Compare *ram blowout preventer*.

annular space *n*: the space between two concentric circles. In the petroleum industry, it is usually the space surrounding a pipe in the wellbore; sometimes termed the annulus.

annulus *n*: see *annular space*.

antifreeze *n*: a chemical added to liquid that lowers its freezing point. Often used to prevent water in an engine's cooling system from freezing.

automatic choke *n*: an adjustable choke that is power-operated to control pressure of flow. See *adjustable choke*.

auxiliaries *n pl*: equipment on a drilling or workover rig that is not a major part of the rig's drilling equipment, such as the equipment used to generate electricity for rig lighting or the equipment used to mix drilling fluid.

auxiliary brake *n*: a braking mechanism on the drawworks, supplemental to the mechanical brake, that permits the lowering of heavy hook loads safely at retarded rates without incurring appreciable brake maintenance. There are two types of auxiliary brake—the hydrodynamic and the electrodynamic. In both types, work is converted into heat, which is dissipated through liquid cooling systems. See *electrodynamic brake*, *hydrodynamic brake*.

auxiliary equipment *n*: see *auxiliaries*.

B

bail *n*: a curved steel rod on top of the swivel that resembles the handle, or bail, of an ordinary bucket, but is much larger. Just as an ordinary bucket is hung from a hook by its bail, the swivel is hung from the traveling block's hook by its bail. Sometimes, the two steel rods (the links) that attach the elevator to the hook are also called bails. *v*: to recover bottomhole fluids, samples, mud, sand, or drill cuttings by lowering a cylindrical vessel called a bailer to the bottom of a well, filling it, and retrieving it.

bailer *n*: a long, cylindrical container fitted with a valve at its lower end, used to remove water, sand, mud, drilling cuttings, or oil from a well in cable-tool drilling.

bearing *n*: 1. an object, surface, or point that supports. 2. a machine part in which another part (such as a journal or pin) turns or slides.

bit *n*: the cutting or boring element used in drilling oil and gas wells. The bit consists of a cutting element and a circulating element. The cutting element is steel teeth, tungsten carbide buttons, industrial diamonds, or polycrystalline diamonds (PDCs). These teeth, buttons, or diamonds penetrate and gouge or scrape the formation to remove it. The circulating element permits the passage of drilling fluid and utilizes the hydraulic force of the fluid stream to improve drilling rates. Most bits used in rotary drilling are roller cone bits, but diamond bits are also used extensively.

blind ram *n*: an integral part of a blowout preventer, which serves as the closing element on an open hole. Its sealing surfaces do not fit around the drill pipe but seal against each other and shut off the space below completely. See *ram*.

blind ram preventer *n*: a blowout preventer in which blind rams are the closing elements. See *blind ram*.

block *n*: any assembly of pulleys on a common framework; in mechanics, one or more pulleys, or sheaves, mounted to rotate on a common axis. The crown block is an assembly of sheaves mounted on beams at the top of the derrick or mast. See *crown block*, *drilling line*, *traveling block*.

blowout *n*: an uncontrolled flow of gas, oil, or other well fluids into the atmosphere or into an underground formation. A blowout, or gusher, can occur when formation pressure exceeds the pressure applied to it by the column of drilling fluid.

blowout preventer *n*: one of several valves installed at the wellhead to prevent the escape of pressure either in the annular space between the casing and the drill pipe or in open hole (i.e., hole with no drill pipe) during drilling or completion operations. Blowout preventers on land rigs are located beneath the rig at the land's surface; on jackup or platform rigs, at the water's surface; and on floating offshore rigs, on the seafloor. See *annular blowout preventer, inside blowout preventer, ram blowout preventer*.

blowout preventer control panel *n*: controls, usually located near the driller's position on the rig floor, that are manipulated to open and close the blowout preventers. See *blowout preventer*.

blowout preventer control unit *n*: a device that stores hydraulic fluid under pressure in special containers and provides a method to open and close the blowout preventers quickly and reliably. Usually, compressed air and hydraulic pressure provide the opening and closing force in the unit. See *blowout preventer*.

bomb *n*: a thick-walled container, usually steel, used to hold devices that determine and record pressure or temperature in a wellbore. See *bottomhole pressure*.

BOP *abbr*: blowout preventer.

borehole *n*: a hole made by drilling or boring; a wellbore.

bottomhole choke *n*: a device with a restricted opening placed in the lower end of the tubing to control the rate of flow. See *choke*.

bottomhole pressure *n*: 1. the pressure at the bottom of a borehole. It is caused by the hydrostatic pressure of the wellbore fluid and, sometimes, by any back-pressure held at the surface, as when the well is shut in with blowout preventers. When mud is being circulated, bottomhole pressure is the hydrostatic pressure plus the remaining circulating pressure required to move the mud up the annulus. 2. the pressure in a well at a point opposite the producing formation, as recorded by a bottomhole pressure bomb.

box *n*: the female section of a connection. See *tool joint*.

box and pin *n*: see *tool joint*.

brake *n*: a device for arresting the motion of a mechanism, usually by means of friction, as in the drawworks brake. Compare *electrodynamic brake, hydrodynamic brake*.

break *v*: to begin or start (e.g., to break circulation or break tour).

break out *v*: 1. to unscrew one section of pipe from another section, especially drill pipe while it is being withdrawn from the wellbore. During this operation, the tongs are used to start the unscrewing operation. 2. to separate, as gas from a liquid or water from an emulsion.

breakout cathead *n*: a device attached to the catshaft of the drawworks that is used as a power source for unscrewing drill pipe; usually located opposite the driller's side of the drawworks. See *cathead*.

breakout tongs *n pl*: tongs that are used to start unscrewing one section of pipe from another section, especially drill pipe coming out of the hole. See *lead tongs, tongs*.

break tour (pronounced "tower") *v*: to begin operating 24 hours a day. Moving the rig and rigging up are usually carried on during daylight hours only. When the rig is ready for operation at a new location, crews break tour.

C

cable *n*: a rope of wire, hemp, or other strong fibers. See *wire rope*.

cable-tool drilling *n*: a drilling method in which the hole is drilled by dropping a sharply pointed bit on bottom. The bit is attached to a cable, and the cable is repeatedly dropped as the hole is drilled.

cased *adj*: pertaining to a wellbore in which casing has been run and cemented. See *casing*.

cased hole *n*: a wellbore in which casing has been run.

casing *n*: 1. steel pipe placed in an oil or gas well to prevent the wall of the hole from caving in, to prevent movement of fluids from one formation to another, and to improve the efficiency of extracting petroleum if the well is productive. A joint of casing is available in three length ranges: a joint of range 1 casing is 16 to 25 feet (4.8 to 7.6 metres) long; a joint of range 2 casing is 25 to 34 feet (7.6 to 10.3 metres) long; and a joint of range 3 casing is 34 to 48 feet (10.3 to 14.6 metres) long. Diameters of casing manufactured to API specifications range from $4^1/_2$ to 20 inches (11.4 to 50.8 centimetres). Casing is also made of many types of steel alloy, which vary in strength, corrosion resistance, and so on. 2. large pipe in which a carrier pipeline is contained. Casing is used when a pipeline passes under railroad rights-of-way and some roads to shield the pipeline from the unusually high load stresses of a particular location. State and local regulations identify specific locations where casing is mandatory.

casinghead *n*: a heavy, flanged steel fitting connected to the first string of casing. It provides a housing for slips and packing assemblies, allows suspension of intermediate and production strings of casing, and supplies the means for the annulus to be sealed off. Also called a spool.

casing string *n*: the entire length of all the joints of casing run in a well. Most casing joints are manufactured to specifications established by API, although non-API specification casing is available for special situations. Casing manufactured to API specifications is available in three length ranges. A joint of range 1 casing is 16 to 25 feet (4.8 to 7.6 metres) long; a joint of range 2 casing is 25 to 34 feet (7.6 to 10.3 metres) long; and a joint of range 3 casing is 34 to 48 feet long (10.3 to 14.6 metres). The outside diameter of a joint of API casing ranges from $4^1/_2$ to 20 inches (11.43 to 50.8 centimetres).

cathead *n*: 1. a spool-shaped attachment on the end of the catshaft, around which rope for hoisting and moving heavy equipment on or near the rig floor is wound. 2. an automatic cathead. See *breakout cathead, makeup cathead*.

cathead spool *n*: see *cathead*.

catline *n*: a hoisting or pulling line powered by the cathead and used to lift heavy equipment on the rig. See *cathead*.

catshaft *n*: an axle that crosses through the drawworks and contains a revolving spool called a cathead at either end. See *cathead*.

cementing *n*: the application of a liquid slurry of cement and water to various points inside or outside the casing.

chain and gear drive *n*: see *chain drive*.

chain drive *n*: a mechanical drive using a driving chain and chain gears to transmit power. Power transmissions use a roller chain, in which each link is made of side bars, transverse pins, and rollers on the pins. A double roller chain is made of two connected rows of links, a triple roller chain of three, and so forth.

choke *n*: a device with an orifice installed in a line to restrict the flow of fluids. Surface chokes are part of the Christmas tree on a well and contain a choke nipple, or bean, with a small-diameter bore that serves to restrict the flow. Chokes are also used to control the rate of flow of the drilling mud out of the hole when the well is closed in with the blowout preventer and a kick is being circulated out of the hole.

choke line *n*: a pipe attached to the blowout preventer stack out of which kick fluids and mud can be pumped to the choke manifold when a blowout preventer is closed in on a kick.

choke manifold *n*: an arrangement of piping and special valves, called chokes. In drilling, mud is circulated through a choke manifold when the blowout preventers are closed. In well testing, a choke manifold attached to the wellhead allows flow and pressure control for test components downstream.

Christmas tree *n*: the control valves, pressure gauges, and chokes assembled at the top of a well to control the flow of oil and gas after the well has been drilled and completed. It is used when reservoir pressure is sufficient to cause reservoir fluids to flow to the surface.

circulate *v*: to pass from one point throughout a system and back to the starting point. For example, drilling fluid is circulated out of the suction pit, down the drill pipe and drill collars, out the bit, up the annulus, and back to the pits while drilling proceeds.

circulating components *n pl*: the equipment included in the drilling fluid circulating system of a rotary rig. Basically, the components consist of the mud pump, rotary hose, swivel, drill stem, bit, and mud return line.

circulating fluid *n*: also called drilling mud. See *drilling fluid, mud*.

clutch *n*: a coupling used to connect and disconnect a driving and a driven part of a mechanism, especially a coupling that permits the former part to engage the latter gradually and without shock. In the oilfield, a clutch permits gradual engaging and disengaging of the equipment driven by a prime mover. *v*: to engage or disengage a clutch.

company representative *n*: an employee of an operating company whose job is to represent the company's interests at the drilling location.

compound *n*: 1. a mechanism used to transmit power from the engines to the pump, the drawworks, and other machinery on a drilling rig. It is composed of clutches, chains and sprockets, belts and pulleys, and a number of shafts, both driven and driving. 2. a substance formed by the chemical union of two or more elements in definite proportions; the smallest particle of a chemical compound is a molecule. *v*: to connect two or more power-producing devices, such as engines, to run driven equipment, such as the drawworks.

contract depth *n*: the depth of the wellbore at which a drilling contract is fulfilled.

crew *n*: 1. the workers on a drilling or workover rig, including the driller, derrickman, and rotary helpers. 2. any group of oilfield workers.

crown block *n*: an assembly of sheaves mounted on beams at the top of the derrick or mast and over which the drilling line is reeved. See *block*.

D

daylight tour (pronounced "tower") *n*: in areas where three 8-hour tours are worked, the shift of duty on a drilling rig that starts at or about daylight. Compare *evening tour* and *graveyard tour*.

deadline *n*: the drilling line from the crown block sheave to the anchor, so called because it does not move. Compare *fastline*.

deadline anchor *n*: see *deadline tie-down anchor*.

deadline tie-down anchor *n*: a device to which the deadline is attached, securely fastened to the mast or derrick substructure. Also called a deadline anchor.

deadman *n*: 1. a buried anchor to which guy wires are tied to steady the derrick, mast, stacks, and so on. 2. an anchoring point against which the winch on a boring machine for pipelining can pull.

degasser *n*: the device used to remove unwanted gas from a liquid, especially from drilling fluid.

derrick *n*: a large load-bearing structure, usually of bolted construction. In drilling, the standard derrick has four legs standing at the corners of the substructure and reaching to the crown block. The substructure is an assembly of heavy beams used to elevate the derrick and provide space to install blowout preventers, casingheads, and so forth. Because the standard derrick must be assembled piece by piece, it has largely been replaced by the mast, which can be lowered and raised without disassembly.

derrick floor *n*: also called the rig floor or the drill floor. See *rig floor*.

derrickhand *n*: the crew member who handles the upper end of the drill string as it is being hoisted out of or lowered into the hole. He or she is also responsible for the circulating machinery and the conditioning of the drilling fluid.

desander *n*: a centrifugal device for removing sand from drilling fluid to prevent abrasion of the pumps. It may be operated mechanically or by a fast-moving stream of fluid inside a special cone-shaped vessel, in which case it is sometimes called a hydrocyclone. Compare *desilter*.

desilter *n*: a centrifugal device for removing very fine particles, or silt, from drilling fluid to keep the amount of solids in the fluid at the lowest possible point. Usually, the lower the solids content of mud, the faster is the rate of penetration. The desilter works on the same principle as a desander. Compare *desander*.

diamond bit *n*: a drill bit that has small industrial diamonds embedded in its cutting surface. Cutting is performed by the rotation of the very hard diamonds over the rock surface.

diesel-electric power *n*: the power supplied to a drilling rig by diesel engines driving electric generators; used widely.

diesel engine *n*: a high-compression, internal-combustion engine used extensively for powering drilling rigs. In a diesel engine, air is drawn into the cylinders and compressed to very high pressures; ignition occurs as fuel is injected into the compressed and heated air. Combustion takes place within the cylinder above the piston, and expansion of the combustion products imparts power to the piston.

direct current (DC) *n*: electric current that flows in only one direction. Compare *alternating current*.

discharge line *n*: a line through which drilling mud travels from the mud pump to the standpipe on its way to the wellbore.

double *n*: a length of drill pipe, casing, or tubing consisting of two joints screwed together. Compare *fourble*, *single*, *thribble*.

drag bit *n*: any of a variety of drilling bits that have no moving parts. As they are rotated on bottom, elements of the bit make hole by being pressed into the formation and being dragged across it.

drawworks *n*: the hoisting mechanism on a drilling rig. It is essentially a large winch that spools off or takes in the drilling line and thus raises or lowers the drill stem and bit.

drawworks brake *n*: the mechanical brake on the drawworks that can prevent the drawworks drum from moving.

drill *v*: to bore a hole in the earth, usually to find and remove subsurface formation fluids such as oil and gas.

drill bit *n*: the cutting or boring element used for drilling. See *bit*.

drill collar *n*: a heavy, thick-walled tube, usually steel, placed between the drill pipe and the bit in the drill stem. Several drill collars are used to provide weight on the bit and to provide a pendulum effect to the drill stem. When manufactured to API specifications, a drill collar joint is 30 or 31 feet (9.1 or 9.4 metres) long. The outside diameter of drill collars made to API specifications ranges from 3½ inches to 11 inches (7.9 to 27.9 centimetres).

driller *n*: the employee directly in charge of a drilling or workover rig and crew. The driller's main duty is operation of the drilling and hoisting equipment, but this crew member is also responsible for downhole condition of the well, operation of downhole tools, and pipe measurements.

driller's BOP control panel *n*: a series of controls on the rig floor that the driller manipulates to open and close the blowout preventers.

driller's console *n*: a metal cabinet on the rig floor containing the controls that the driller manipulates to operate various components of the drilling rig.

driller's control panel *n*: see *driller's console*.

driller's panel *n*: see *driller's console*.

drilling contractor *n*: an individual or group that owns a drilling rig or rigs and contracts services for drilling wells.

drilling fluid *n*: circulating fluid, one function of which is to lift cuttings out of the wellbore and to the surface. Other functions are to cool the bit and to counteract downhole formation pressure. Although a mixture of barite, clay, water, and chemical additives is the most common drilling fluid, wells can also be drilled by using air, gas, water, or oil-base mud as the drilling mud. See *mud*.

drilling hook *n*: the large hook mounted on the bottom of the traveling block and from which the swivel is suspended. When drilling, the entire weight of the drill stem is suspended from the hook.

drilling line *n*: a wire rope used to support the drilling tools. Also called the rotary line.

drilling mud *n*: a specially compounded liquid circulated through the wellbore during rotary drilling operations. See *drilling fluid, mud*.

drilling superintendent *n*: an employee, usually of a drilling contractor, who is in charge of all drilling operations that the contractor is engaged in.

drill pipe *n*: seamless steel or aluminum pipe made up in the drill stem between the kelly or top drive on the surface and the drill collars on the bottom. Several joints are made up (screwed together) to form the drill string.

drill stem *n*: all members in the assembly used for rotary drilling from the swivel to the bit, including the kelly, drill pipe and tool joints, drill collars, stabilizers, and various specialty items. Compare *drill string*.

drill string *n*: the column, or string, of drill pipe with attached tool joints that transmits fluid and rotational power from the kelly to the drill collars and bit. Often, especially in the oil patch, the term is loosely applied to both drill pipe and drill collars. Compare *drill stem*.

drive *n*: 1. the means by which a machine is given motion or power, or by which power is transferred from one part of a machine to another. 2. the energy of expanding gas, inflowing water, or other natural or artificial mechanisms that forces crude oil out of the reservoir formation and into the wellbore. *v*: to give motion or power.

drive bushing *n*: see *kelly bushing*.

duplex pump *n*: a reciprocating pump with two pistons or plungers and used extensively as a mud pump on drilling rigs.

E

electric drive *n*: see *electric rig*.

electric-drive rig *n*: see *electric rig*.

electric generator *n*: a machine by which mechanical energy is changed into electrical energy, such as an electric generator on a drilling rig in which a diesel engine (mechanical power) turns a generator to make electricity (electrical energy).

electrician *n*: the rig crew member who maintains and repairs the electrical generation and distribution system on the rig.

electric rig *n*: a drilling rig on which the energy from the power source—usually several diesel engines—is changed to electricity by generators mounted on the engines. The electrical power is then distributed through electrical conductors to electric motors. The motors power the various rig components. Compare *mechanical rig*.

electrodynamic brake *n*: a device mounted on the end of the drawworks shaft of a drilling rig. The electrodynamic brake (sometimes called a magnetic brake) serves as an auxiliary to the mechanical brake when pipe is lowered into a well. The braking effect in an electrodynamic brake is achieved by means of the interaction of electric currents with magnets, with other currents, or with themselves.

elevators *n pl*: clamps that grip a stand of casing, tubing, drill pipe, or sucker rods so that the stand can be raised from or lowered into the hole.

evening tour (pronounced "tower") *n*: the shift of duty on a drilling rig that starts in the afternoon and runs through the evening. Sometimes called afternoon tour. Compare *daylight tour, graveyard tour*.

F

fastline *n*: the end of the drilling line that is affixed to the drum or reel of the drawworks, so called because it travels with greater velocity than any other portion of the line. Compare *deadline*.

fast sheave *n*: that sheave on the crown block over which the fastline is reeved.

fixed choke *n*: a choke whose opening is one size only, that is, not adjustable. Compare *adjustable choke*.

floor crew *n*: those workers on a drilling or workover rig who work primarily on the rig floor.

floorhand *n*: see *rotary helper*.

fluid *n*: a substance that flows and yields to any force tending to change its shape. Liquids and gases are fluids.

formation *n*: a bed or deposit composed throughout of substantially the same kind of rock; often a lithologic unit. Each formation is given a name, frequently as a result of the study of the formation outcrop at the surface and sometimes based on fossils found in the formation.

formation fluid *n*: fluid (such as gas, oil, or water) that exists in a subsurface rock formation.

formation pressure *n*: the force exerted by fluids in a formation, recorded in the hole at the level of the formation with the well shut in. Also called reservoir pressure or shut-in bottomhole pressure.

fourble *n*: a section of drill pipe, casing, or tubing consisting of four joints screwed together. Compare *double, single, thribble*.

full-gauge bit *n*: a bit that has maintained its original diameter.

full-gauge hole *n*: a wellbore drilled with a full-gauge bit. Also called a true-to-gauge hole.

G

gas *n*: a compressible fluid that completely fills any container in which it is confined. Technically, a gas will not condense when it is compressed and cooled, because a gas can exist only above the critical temperature for its particular composition. Below the critical temperature, this form of matter is known as a vapor, because liquid can exist and condensation can occur. Sometimes the terms "gas" and "vapor" are used interchangeably. The latter, however, should be used for those streams in which condensation can occur and that originate from, or are in equilibrium with, a liquid phase.

gooseneck *n*: the curved connection between the rotary hose and the swivel. See *swivel*.

graveyard tour (pronounced "tower") *n*: the shift of duty on a drilling rig that starts at midnight. Sometimes called the morning tour.

ground anchor *n*: see *deadman*.

guy line *n*: a wireline attached to a mast, derrick, or offshore platform to stabilize it. See *load guy line, wind guy line*.

H

hoist *n*: 1. an arrangement of pulleys and wire rope or chain used for lifting heavy objects; a winch or similar device. 2. the drawworks. *v*: to raise or lift.

hoisting components *n pl*: drawworks, drilling line, and traveling and crown blocks. Auxiliary hoisting components include catheads, catshaft, and air hoist.

hoisting drum *n*: the large flanged spool in the drawworks on which the hoisting cable is wound. See *drawworks*.

hole *n*: in drilling operations, the wellbore or borehole. See *borehole, wellbore*.

hook *n*: a large, hook-shaped device from which the swivel is suspended. It is designed to carry maximum loads ranging from 100 to 650 tons (90 to 590 tonnes) and turns on bearings in its supporting housing. A strong spring within the assembly cushions the weight of a stand (90 feet, about 27 metres) of drill pipe, thus permitting the pipe to be made up and broken out with less damage to the tool joint threads. Smaller hooks without the spring are used for handling tubing and sucker rods. See *stand* and *swivel*.

hydraulic brake *n*: also called hydrodynamic brake or Hydromatic® brake. See *hydrodynamic brake*.

hydraulic fluid *n*: a liquid of low viscosity (such as light oil) that is used in systems actuated by liquid (such as the brake system in a modern passenger car).

hydrocarbons *n pl*: organic compounds of hydrogen and carbon whose densities, boiling points, and freezing points increase as their molecular weights increase. Although composed of only two elements, hydrocarbons exist in a variety of compounds, because of the strong affinity of the carbon atom for other atoms and for itself. The smallest molecules of hydrocarbons are gaseous; the largest are solids. Petroleum is a mixture of many different hydrocarbons.

hydrodynamic brake *n*: a device mounted on the end of the drawworks shaft of a drilling rig. It serves as an auxiliary to the mechanical brake when pipe is lowered into the well. The braking effect is achieved by means of an impeller turning in a housing filled with water. Sometimes called hydraulic brake or Hydromatic® brake.

I

inside blowout preventer *n*: any one of several types of valve installed in the drill stem to prevent a blowout through the stem. Flow is possible only downward, allowing mud to be pumped in but preventing any flow back up the stem. Also called an internal blowout preventer.

J

jackknife mast *n*: a structural steel, open-sided tower raised vertically by special lifting tackle attached to the traveling block. See *mast*. Compare *standard derrick*.

jackknife rig *n*: a drilling rig that has a jackknife mast instead of a standard derrick.

jackup *n*: a mobile bottom-supported offshore drilling structure with columnar or open-truss legs that support the deck and hull. When positioned over the drilling site, the bottoms of the legs rest on the seafloor. A jackup rig is towed or propelled to a location with its legs up. Once the legs are firmly positioned on the bottom, the deck and hull height are adjusted and leveled. Also called self-elevating drilling unit.

jet bit *n*: a drilling bit having replaceable nozzles through which the drilling fluid is directed in a high-velocity stream to the bottom of the hole to improve the efficiency of the bit. See *bit*.

joint *n*: 1. in drilling, a single length (from 16 feet to 45 feet, or 5 metres to 14.5 metres, depending on its range length) of drill pipe, drill collar, casing, or tubing that has threaded connections at both ends. Several joints screwed together constitute a stand of pipe. 2. in pipelining, a single length (usually 40 feet—12 metres) of pipe. 3. in geology, a crack or fissure produced in a rock by internal stresses. 4. in sucker rod pumping, a single length of sucker rod that has threaded connections at both ends.

K

kelly *n*: the heavy steel tubular device, three-, four-, six-, or eight-sided, suspended from the swivel through the rotary table and connected to the top joint of drill pipe to turn the drill stem as the rotary table turns. It has a bored passageway that permits fluid to be circulated into the drill stem and up the annulus, or the reverse. Kellys manufactured to API specifications are available only in four- or six-sided versions, are either 40 or 54 feet (12 to 16 metres) long, and have diameters as small as $2\frac{1}{2}$ inches (6 centimetres) and as large as 6 inches (15 centimetres).

kelly bushing (KB) *n*: a special device placed around the kelly that mates with the kelly flats and fits into the master bushing of the rotary table. The kelly bushing is designed so that the kelly is free to move up or down through it. The bottom of the bushing may be shaped to fit the opening in the master bushing or it may have pins that fit into the master bushing. In either case, when the kelly bushing is inserted into the master bushing and the master bushing is turned, the kelly bushing also turns. Since the kelly bushing fits onto the kelly, the kelly turns, and since the kelly is made up to the drill stem, the drill stem turns. Also called the drive bushing.

kelly cock *n*: a valve installed at one or both ends of the kelly that is closed when a high-pressure backflow begins inside the drill stem. The valve is closed to keep pressure off the swivel and rotary hose.

kelly flat *n*: one of the flat sides of a kelly. Also called a flat.

kelly hose *n*: also called the mud hose or rotary hose. See *rotary hose*.

kelly joint *n*: see *kelly*.

kick *n*: an entry of water, gas, oil, or other formation fluid into the wellbore during drilling. It occurs because the pressure exerted by the column of drilling fluid is not great enough to overcome the pressure exerted by the fluids in the formation drilled. If prompt action is not taken to control the kick, or kill the well, a blowout may occur.

kick fluids *n pl*: oil, gas, water, or any combination that enters the borehole from a permeable formation.

kill *v*: 1. in drilling, to control a kick by taking suitable preventive measures (e.g., to shut in the well with the blowout preventers, circulate the kick out, and increase the weight of the drilling mud). 2. in production, to stop a well from producing oil and gas so that reconditioning of the well can proceed. Production is stopped by circulating a kill fluid into the hole.

kill fluid *n*: drilling mud of a weight great enough to equal or exceed the pressure exerted by formation fluids.

lead tongs (pronounced "leed") *n pl*: the pipe tongs suspended in the derrick or mast and operated by a wireline connected to the breakout cathead. In coming out of the hole, they are used on the pin end of the joint for breaking out. In going into the hole, they are used on the box end as backup to the makeup tongs. In some areas, personnel call the makeup tongs the lead tongs if pipe is going into the hole; similarly, they call the breakout tongs the lead tongs if pipe is coming out of the hole.

line *n*: 1. any length of pipe through which liquid or gas flows. 2. rope or wire rope. 3. electrical wire.

liquid *n*: a state of matter in which the shape of the given mass depends on the containing vessel, but the volume of the mass is independent of the vessel. A liquid is a fluid that is almost incompressible.

load guy line *n*: the wireline attached to a mast or derrick to provide the main support for the structure. Compare *wind guy line*.

lower kelly cock *n*: a special valve normally installed below the kelly. Usually, the valve is open so that drilling fluid can flow out of the kelly and down the drill stem. It can, however, be manually closed with a special wrench when necessary. In one case, the valve is closed and broken out, still attached to the kelly to prevent drilling mud in the kelly from draining onto the rig floor. In another case, when kick pressure inside the drill stem exists, the drill stem safety valve is closed to prevent the pressure from escaping up the drill stem.

lower kelly valve *n*: see *lower kelly cock*.

make a connection *v*: to attach a joint of drill pipe onto the drill stem suspended in the wellbore to permit deepening the wellbore by the length of the joint added (about 30 feet, or 9 metres).

make a trip *v*: to hoist the drill stem out of the wellbore to perform one of a number of operations, such as changing bits or taking a core, and then to return the drill stem to the wellbore.

make up *v*: 1. to assemble and join parts to form a complete unit (e.g., to make up a string of casing). 2. to screw together two threaded pieces. 3. to mix or prepare (e.g., to make up a tank of mud). 4. to compensate for (e.g., to make up for lost time).

makeup cathead *n*: a device that is attached to the shaft of the drawworks and used as a power source for screwing together joints of pipe. It is usually located on the driller's side of the drawworks. Also called spinning cathead. See *cathead*.

makeup tongs *n pl*: tongs used for screwing one length of pipe into another for making up a joint. See *lead tongs, tongs*.

male connection *n*: a pipe, coupling, or tool that has threads on the outside so that it can be joined to a female connection.

mast *n*: a portable derrick that is capable of being raised as a unit, as distinguished from a standard derrick, which cannot be raised to a working position as a unit. For transporting by land, the mast can be divided into two or more sections to avoid excessive length extending from truck beds on the highway. Compare *derrick*.

master bushing *n*: a device that fits into the rotary table to accommodate the slips and drive the kelly bushing so that the rotating motion of the rotary table can be transmitted to the kelly. Also called rotary bushing.

master control panel *n*: on a drilling rig, the primary station that controls the operation of the blowout preventers and other well-control equipment. Also called primary control panel. Backup control panels are usually installed should the master panel fail, or should it become inaccessible. See also *driller's BOP control panel*.

mechanic *n*: an optional crew member who is an all-around repairer for the rig's mechanical components.

mechanical brake *n*: a brake that is actuated by machinery (such as levers or rods) that is directly linked to it.

mechanical rig *n*: a drilling rig in which the source of power is one or more internal-combustion engines and in which the power is distributed to rig components through mechanical devices (such as chains, sprockets, clutches, and shafts). Also called a power rig.

mix mud *v*: to prepare drilling fluids from a mixture of water or other liquids and any one or more of the various dry mud-making materials (such as clay, weighting materials, and chemicals).

monkeyboard *n*: the derrickhand's working platform. As pipe or tubing is run into or out of the hole, the derrickhand must handle the top end of the pipe, which may be as high as 90 feet (27 metres) in the derrick or mast. The monkeyboard provides a small platform to raise him or her to the proper height for handling the top of the pipe.

morning tour (pronounced "tower") *n*: see *graveyard tour*. Compare *daylight tour, evening tour*.

motorhand *n*: the crew member on a rotary drilling rig, usually the most experienced rotary helper, who is responsible for the care and operation of drilling engines.

mousehole *n*: an opening through the rig floor, usually lined with pipe, into which a length of drill pipe is placed temporarily for later connection to the drill string.

mousehole connection *n*: the procedure of adding a length of drill pipe or tubing to the active string. The length to be added is placed in the mousehole, made up to the kelly, then pulled out of the mousehole and subsequently made up into the string. Compare *rathole connection*.

mud *n*: the liquid circulated through the wellbore during rotary drilling and workover operations. In addition to its function of bringing cuttings to the surface, drilling mud cools and lubricates the bit and drill stem, protects against blowouts by holding back subsurface pressures, and deposits a mud cake on the wall of the borehole to prevent loss of fluids to the formation. Although it was originally a suspension of earth solids (especially clays) in water, the mud used in modern drilling operations is a more complex, three-phase mixture of liquids, reactive solids, and inert solids. The liquid phase may be fresh water, diesel oil, or crude oil and may contain one or more conditioners. See *drilling fluid*.

mud additive *n*: any material added to drilling fluid to change some of its characteristics or properties.

mud circulation *n*: the process of pumping mud downward to the bit and back up to the surface in a drilling or workover operation.

mud column *n*: the borehole when it is filled or partially filled with drilling mud.

mud conditioning *n*: the treatment and control of drilling mud to ensure that it has the correct properties. Conditioning may include the use of additives, the removal of sand or other solids, the removal of gas, the addition of water, and other measures to prepare the mud for conditions encountered in a specific well.

mud-gas separator *n*: a device that removes gas from the mud coming out of a well when a kick is being circulated out.

mud pump *n*: a large, high-pressure reciprocating pump used to circulate the mud on a drilling rig. A typical mud pump is a two-cylinder double-acting or a three-cylinder single-acting piston pump whose pistons travel in replaceable liners and are driven by a crankshaft actuated by an engine or a motor. Also called a slush pump.

mud system *n*: the composition and characteristics of the drilling mud used on a particular well.

mud tank *n*: one of a series of open tanks, usually made of steel plate, through which the drilling mud is cycled to remove sand and fine sediments. Additives are mixed with the mud in the tanks, and the fluid is temporarily stored there before being pumped back into the well. Modern rotary drilling rigs are generally provided with three or more tanks, fitted with built-in piping, valves, and mud agitators. Also called mud pits.

mud weight *n*: a measure of the density of a drilling fluid expressed as pounds per gallon, pounds per cubic foot, or kilograms per cubic metre. Mud weight is directly related to the amount of pressure the column of drilling mud exerts at the bottom of the hole.

N

natural gas *n*: a highly compressible, highly expansible mixture of hydrocarbons with a low specific gravity and occurring naturally in a gaseous form. Besides hydrocarbon gases, natural gas may contain appreciable quantities of nitrogen, helium, carbon dioxide, hydrogen sulfide, and water vapor. Although gaseous at normal temperatures and pressures, the gases making up the mixture that is natural gas are variable in form and may be found either as gases or as liquids under suitable conditions of temperature and pressure.

nozzle *n*: 1. a passageway through jet bits that causes the drilling fluid to be ejected from the bit at high velocity. The jets of mud clear the bottom of the hole. Nozzles come in different sizes that can be interchanged on the bit to adjust the velocity with which the mud exits the bit. 2. the part of the fuel system of an engine that has small holes in it to permit fuel to enter the cylinder. Properly known as a fuel-injection nozzle, but also called a spray valve. The needle valve is directly above the nozzle.

O **oil** *n*: a simple or complex liquid mixture of hydrocarbons that can be refined to yield gasoline, kerosene, diesel fuel, and various other products.

oil and gas separator *n*: an item of production equipment used to separate liquid components of the well fluid from gaseous elements. Separators are either vertical or horizontal and either cylindrical or spherical. Separation is accomplished principally by gravity, the heavier liquids falling to the bottom and the gas rising to the top. A float valve or other liquid-level control regulates the level of oil in the bottom of the separator.

oil-base mud *n*: a drilling or workover fluid in which oil is the continuous phase and which contains from less than 2 percent and up to 5 percent water. This water is spread out, or dispersed, in the oil as small droplets.

oilfield *n*: the surface area overlying an oil reservoir or reservoirs. The term usually includes not only the surface area, but also the reservoir, the wells, and the production equipment.

open hole *n*: 1. any wellbore in which casing has not been set. 2. open or cased hole in which no drill pipe or tubing is suspended. 3. the portion of the wellbore that has no casing.

open-hole completion *n*: a method of preparing a well for production in which no production casing or liner is set opposite the producing formation. Reservoir fluids flow unrestricted into the open wellbore. An open-hole completion has limited use in rather special situations. Also called a barefoot completion.

operating company *n*: see *operator*.

operator *n*: the person or company, either proprietor or lessee, actually operating an oilwell or lease, generally the oil company that engages the drilling contractor.

out-of-gauge bit *n*: a bit that is no longer of the proper diameter.

out-of-gauge hole *n*: a hole that is not in gauge; that is, it is smaller or larger than the diameter of the bit used to drill it.

overgauge hole *n*: a hole whose diameter is larger than the diameter of the bit used to drill it. An overgauge hole can occur when a bit is not properly stabilized or does not have enough weight put on it or because of erosion caused by jet bit hydraulics or high annular velocities.

P **PDC bit** *n*: a special type of diamond drilling bit that does not use roller cones. Instead, polycrystalline diamond inserts are embedded into a matrix on the bit.

petroleum *n*: a substance occurring naturally in the earth in solid, liquid, or gaseous state and composed mainly of mixtures of chemical compounds of carbon and hydrogen, with or without other nonmetallic elements such as sulfur, oxygen, and nitrogen. In some cases, especially in the measurement of oil and gas, petroleum refers only to oil—a liquid hydrocarbon—and does not include natural gas or gas liquids such as propane and butane. The API Measurement Coordination Department prefers that petroleum mean crude oil and not natural gas or gas liquids.

pin *n*: 1. the male section of a tool joint. 2. on a bit, the bit shank. 3. one of the pegs that are fitted on each side into the link plates (side bars) of a chain link of roller chain and that serve as the stable members onto which bushings are press-fitted and around which rollers move.

pipe *n*: a long, hollow cylinder, usually steel, through which fluids are conducted. Oilfield tubular goods are casing (including liners), drill pipe, tubing, or line pipe.

pipe fitting *n*: an auxiliary part (such as a coupling, elbow, tee, or cross) used for connecting lengths of pipe.

pipe rack *n*: a horizontal support for tubular goods.

pipe racker *n*: 1. (obsolete) a worker who places pipe to one side in the derrick. 2. a pneumatic or hydraulic device often used on drill ships that, on command from an operator, either picks up pipe from a rack and lifts it into the derrick or takes pipe from out of the derrick and places it on the rack. It eliminates the need to stand pipe in the derrick or mast while it is out of the hole, which is desirable for maintaining the vessel's center of gravity as low as possible and for minimizing the possibility of capsizing.

pipe-racking fingers *n pl*: extensions within a pipe rack for keeping individual pipes separated.

pipe ram *n*: a sealing component for a blowout preventer that closes the annular space between the pipe and the blowout preventer or wellhead.

pipe ram preventer *n*: a blowout preventer that uses pipe rams as the closing elements. See *pipe ram*.

pipe tongs *n pl*: see *tongs*.

pit *n*: 1. a temporary containment, usually excavated earth, for wellbore fluids. 2. a mud tank. 3. a reserve pit.

power tongs *n pl*: a wrench that is used to make up or break out drill pipe, tubing, or casing on which the torque is provided by air or fluid pressure.

pressure *n*: the force that a fluid (liquid or gas) exerts uniformly in all directions within a vessel, pipe, hole in the ground, and so forth, such as that exerted against the inner wall of a tank or that exerted on the bottom of the wellbore by a fluid. Pressure is expressed in terms of force exerted per unit of area, as pounds per square inch, or in kilopascals.

preventer *n*: shortened form of blowout preventer. See *blowout preventer*.

prime mover *n*: an internal-combustion engine or a turbine that is the source of power for driving a machine or machines.

production *n*: 1. the phase of the petroleum industry that deals with bringing the well fluids to the surface and separating them and with storing, gauging, and otherwise preparing the product for the pipeline. 2. the amount of oil or gas produced in a given period.

pulley *n*: a wheel with a grooved rim, used for pulling or hoisting. See *sheave*.

pump *n*: a device that increases the pressure on a fluid or raises it to a higher level. Various types of pumps include the bottomhole pump, centrifugal pump, hydraulic pump, jet pump, mud pump, reciprocating pump, rotary pump, sucker rod pump, and submersible pump.

pump manifold *n*: an arrangement of valves and piping that permits a wide choice in the routing of suction and discharge fluids among two or more pumps.

R

rack *n*: 1. framework for supporting or containing a number of loose objects, such as pipe. See *pipe rack*. 2. a bar with teeth on one face for gearing with a pinion or worm gear. 3. a notched bar used as a ratchet. *v*: 1. to place on a rack. 2. to use as a rack.

rack pipe *v*: 1. to place pipe withdrawn from the hole on a pipe rack. 2. to stand pipe on the derrick floor when pulling it out of the hole.

ram *n*: the closing and sealing component on a blowout preventer. One of three types—blind, pipe, or shear—may be installed in several preventers mounted in a stack on top of the wellbore. Blind rams, when closed, form a seal on a hole that has no drill pipe in it; pipe rams, when closed, seal around the pipe; shear rams cut through drill pipe and then form a seal.

ram blowout preventer *n*: a blowout preventer that uses rams to seal off pressure on a hole that is with or without pipe. Also called a ram preventer.

ram preventer *n*: see *ram blowout preventer*.

range length *n*: a grouping of pipe lengths. API designation of range lengths is as follows:

	Range 1 (ft/m)	**Range 2 (ft/m)**	**Range 3 (ft/m)**
Casing	16–25/4.88–7.62	25–34/7.62–10.36	34–48/10.36–14.63
Drill pipe	18–22/5.49–6.7	27–30/8.23–9.14	38–45/11.58–13.72
Tubing	20–24/6.10–7.32	28–32/8.53–9.75	

rathole *n*: 1. a hole in the rig floor, 30 to 35 feet (9 to 11 metres) deep, which is lined with casing that projects above the floor and into which the kelly and swivel are placed when hoisting operations are in progress. 2. a hole of a diameter smaller than the main hole and drilled in the bottom of the main hole. *v*: to reduce the size of the wellbore and drill ahead.

rathole connection *n*: the addition of a length of drill pipe or tubing to the active string using the rathole instead of the mousehole, which is the more common connection. The length to be added is placed in the rathole, made up to the kelly, pulled out of the rathole, and made up into the string. Compare *mousehole connection*.

reel *n*: a revolving device (such as a flanged cylinder) for winding or unwinding something flexible (such as rope or wire).

reeve *v*: to pass (as a rope) through a hole or opening in a block or similar device.

reeve the line *v*: to string a wire rope drilling line through the sheaves of the traveling and crown blocks to the hoisting drum.

remote BOP control panel *n*: a device placed on the rig floor that can be operated by the driller to direct air pressure to actuating cylinders that turn the control valves on the main BOP control unit, located a safe distance from the rig.

remote choke panel *n*: a set of controls, usually placed on the rig floor, that is manipulated to control the amount of drilling fluid being circulated through the choke manifold. This procedure is necessary when a kick is being circulated out of a well. See *choke manifold.*

remote control panel *n*: a system of blowout preventer controls, convenient to the driller, which can be used selectively to actuate valves at the master control panel. Also called secondary control panel. See also *driller's BOP control panel.*

rig *n*: the derrick or mast, drawworks, and attendant surface equipment of a drilling or workover unit.

rig down *v*: to dismantle a drilling rig and auxiliary equipment following the completion of drilling operations. Also called tear down.

rig floor *n*: the area immediately around the rotary table and extending to each corner of the derrick or mast, that is, the area immediately above the substructure on which the drawworks, rotary table, and so forth rest. Also called derrick floor, drill floor.

rig manager *n*: an employee of a drilling contractor who is in charge of the entire drilling crew and the drilling rig. Also called toolpusher, drilling foreman, rig supervisor, or rig superintendent.

rig superintendent *n*: see *toolpusher.*

rig supervisor *n*: see *toolpusher.*

rig up *v*: to prepare the drilling rig for making hole, that is, to install tools and machinery before drilling is started.

rock bit *n*: see *roller cone bit.*

roller cone bit *n*: a drilling bit made of two, three, or four cones, or cutters, that are mounted on extremely rugged bearings. The surface of each cone is made of rows of steel teeth or rows of tungsten carbide inserts. Also called rock bit.

rotary *n*: the machine used to impart rotational power to the drill stem while permitting vertical movement of the pipe for rotary drilling. Modern rotary machines have a special component, the rotary or master bushing, to turn the kelly bushing, which permits vertical movement of the kelly while the stem is turning.

rotary bushing *n*: see *master bushing.*

rotary drilling *n*: a drilling method in which a hole is drilled by a rotating bit to which a downward force is applied. The bit is fastened to and rotated by the drill stem, which also provides a passageway through which the drilling fluid is circulated. Additional joints of drill pipe are added as drilling progresses.

rotary helper *n*: a worker on a drilling or workover rig, subordinate to the driller, whose primary work station is on the rig floor. On rotary drilling rigs, there are at least two and usually three or more rotary helpers on each crew. Sometimes called floorhand, floorman, rig crew member, or roughneck.

rotary hose *n*: a reinforced flexible tube on a rotary drilling rig that conducts the drilling fluid from the standpipe to the swivel and kelly. Also called the mud hose or the kelly hose.

rotary line *n*: see *drilling line*.

rotary slips *n pl*: see *slips*.

rotary table *n*: the principal component of a rotary, or rotary machine, used to turn the drill stem and support the drilling assembly. It has a beveled gear arrangement to create the rotational motion and opening into which bushings are fitted to drive and support the drilling assembly.

rotary tongs *n pl*: see *tongs*.

rotating components *n pl*: those parts of the drilling or workover rig that are designed to turn or rotate the drill stem and bit—swivel, kelly, kelly bushing, master bushing, and rotary table.

roughneck *n*: see *rotary helper*.

round trip *n*: the action of pulling out and subsequently running back into the hole a string of drill pipe or tubing. Making a round trip is also called tripping.

roustabout *n*: 1. a worker on an offshore rig who handles the equipment and supplies that are sent to the rig from the shore base. The head roustabout is very often the crane operator. 2. a worker who assists the foreman in the general work around a producing oilwell, usually on the property of the oil company. 3. a helper on a well servicing unit.

S

safety platform *n*: the monkeyboard, or platform on a derrick or mast on which the derrickhand works while wearing a safety harness (attached to the mast or derrick) to prevent falling.

saver sub *n*: a device made up in the drill stem to absorb much of the wear between frequently broken joints (such as between the kelly and the drill pipe).

set back *v*: to place stands of drill pipe and drill collars in a vertical position to one side of the rotary table in the derrick or mast of a drilling or workover rig.

set casing *v*: to run and cement casing at a certain depth in the wellbore. Sometimes called set pipe.

settling pit *n*: a pit that is dug in the earth for the purpose of receiving mud returned from the well and allowing the solids in the mud to settle out. Steel mud tanks are more often used today, along with various auxiliary equipment for controlling solids quickly and efficiently.

settling tank *n*: 1. the steel mud tank in which solid material in mud is allowed to settle out by gravity. It is used only in special situations today, for solids control equipment has superseded such a tank in most cases. Sometimes called a settling pit. 2. a cylindrical vessel on a lease into which produced emulsion is piped and in which water in the emulsion is allowed to settle out of the oil.

shaker *n*: shortened form of shale shaker. See *shale shaker*.

shale shaker *n*: a vibrating screen used to remove cuttings from the circulating fluid in rotary drilling operations. The size of the openings in the screen should be selected carefully to be the smallest size possible to allow 100% flow of the fluid. Also called a shaker.

shear ram *n*: the component in a blowout preventer that cuts, or shears, through drill pipe and forms a seal against well pressure. Shear rams are used in floating offshore drilling operations to provide a quick method of moving the rig away from the hole when there is no time to trip the drill stem out of the hole.

shear ram preventer *n*: a blowout preventer that uses shear rams as closing elements.

sheave (pronounced "shiv") *n*: 1. a grooved pulley. 2. support wheel over which tape, wire, or cable rides.

sheave groove *n*: an individual groove in a sheave.

single *n*: a joint of drill pipe. Compare *double*, *thribble*, and *fourble*.

slips *n pl*: wedge-shaped pieces of metal with teeth or other gripping elements that are used to prevent pipe from slipping down into the hole or to hold pipe in place. Rotary slips fit around the drill pipe and wedge against the master bushing to support the pipe. Power slips are pneumatically or hydraulically actuated devices that allow the crew to dispense with the manual handling of slips when making a connection. Packers and other downhole equipment are secured in position by slips that engage the inner surface of casing.

sloughing (pronounced "sluffing") *n*: collapsing of the walls of the wellbore.

spinning cathead *n*: see *makeup cathead, spinning chain*.

spinning chain *n*: a Y-shaped chain used to spin up (tighten) one joint of drill pipe into another. One end of the chain is attached to the tongs, another end to the spinning cathead, and the third end left free. The free end is wrapped around the tool joint, and the cathead pulls the chain off the joint, causing the joint to spin rapidly and tighten up. After the free end of the chain is pulled off the joint, the tongs are secured in the spot vacated by the chain and continued pull on the chain (and thus on the tongs) by the cathead makes up the joint to final tightness.

spinning wrench *n*: air-powered or hydraulically powered wrench used to spin drill pipe in making or breaking connections.

spin-up *n*: the rapid turning of the drill stem when one length of pipe is being joined to another.

stack *n*: 1. a vertical arrangement of blowout prevention equipment. Also called preventer stack. See *blowout preventer*. 2. the vertical chimneylike installation that is the waste disposal system for unwanted vapor such as flue gases or tail-gas streams.

stand *n*: the connected joints of pipe racked in the derrick or mast during a trip. The usual stand is about 90 feet (about 27 metres) long, which is three lengths of drill pipe screwed together (a thribble).

standard derrick *n*: a derrick that is built piece by piece at the drilling location, as opposed to a jackknife mast, which is preassembled. Standard derricks have been replaced almost totally by jackknife masts.

string *n*: the entire length of casing, tubing, sucker rods, or drill pipe run into a hole.

string up *v*: to thread the drilling line through the sheaves of the crown block and traveling block. One end of the line is secured to the hoisting drum and the other to the derrick substructure.

stripping in *n*: 1. the process of lowering the drill stem into the wellbore when the well is shut in on a kick and when the weight of the drill stem is sufficient to overcome the force of well pressure. 2. the process of putting tubing into a well under pressure.

sub *n*: a short, threaded piece of pipe used to adapt parts of the drilling string that cannot otherwise be screwed together because of differences in thread size or design. A sub (i.e., a substitute) may also perform a special function. Lifting subs are used with drill collars to provide a shoulder to fit the drill pipe elevators; a kelly saver sub is placed between the drill pipe and the kelly to prevent excessive thread wear of the kelly and drill pipe threads; a bent sub is used when drilling a directional hole.

subsea blowout preventer *n*: a blowout preventer placed on the seafloor for use by a floating offshore drilling rig.

substructure *n*: the foundation on which the derrick or mast and usually the drawworks sit. It contains space for storage and well-control equipment.

surface stack *n*: a blowout preventer stack mounted on top of the casing string at or near the surface of the ground or the water. Surface stacks are employed on land rigs and on bottom-supported MODUs.

swivel *n*: a rotary tool that is hung from the rotary hook and traveling block to suspend the drill stem and to permit it to rotate freely. It also provides a connection for the rotary hose and a passageway for the flow of drilling fluid into the drill stem.

T

telescoping derrick *n*: a portable mast that can be erected as a unit, usually by a tackle that hoists the wireline or by hydraulic pistons. The upper section of a telescoping derrick is generally nested (telescoped) inside the lower section of the structure and raised to full height either by the wireline or by a hydraulic system.

thribble *n*: a stand of pipe made up of three joints and handled as a unit. Compare *double, fourble, single*.

thribble board *n*: the name used for the derrickhand's working platform, the monkeyboard, when it is located at a height in the derrick equal to three lengths of pipe joined together.

tongs *n pl*: the large wrenches used to make up or break out drill pipe, casing, tubing, or other pipe; variously called casing tongs, pipe tongs, and so forth, according to the specific use. Power tongs are pneumatically or hydraulically operated tools that serve to spin the pipe up tight and, in some instances, to apply the final makeup torque.

tool joint *n*: a heavy coupling element for drill pipe. It is made of special alloy steel and has coarse, tapered threads and seating shoulders designed to sustain the weight of the drill stem, withstand the strain of frequent coupling and uncoupling, and provide a leakproof seal. The male section of the joint, or the pin, is attached to one end of a length of drill pipe, and the female section, or box, is attached to the other end. The tool joint may be welded to the end of the pipe, screwed on, or both, although most drill pipe now has welded tool joints. A hard-metal facing is often applied in a band around the outside of the tool joint to enable it to resist abrasion from the walls of the borehole.

toolpusher *n*: an employee of a drilling contractor who is in charge of the entire drilling crew and the drilling rig. Also called a drilling foreman, rig manager, rig superintendent, or rig supervisor.

top drive *n*: a device similar to a power swivel that is used in place of the rotary table to turn the drill stem. It also suspends the drill stem in the hole and includes power tongs. Modern top drives combine the elevator, tongs, swivel, and hook.

tour (pronounced "tower") *n*: a working shift for drilling crew or other oilfield workers. Traditionally, the most common tour is 8 hours; the three daily tours are called daylight, evening (or afternoon), and grave-yard (or morning). Sometimes 12-hour tours are used, especially on offshore rigs; they are called simply day tour and night tour.

transmission *n*: the gear or chain arrangement by which power is transmitted from the prime mover to the drawworks, mud pump, or rotary table of a drilling rig.

traveling block *n*: an arrangement of pulleys, or sheaves, through which drilling line is reeved and which moves up and down in the derrick or mast. See *block*.

tricone bit *n*: a type of bit in which three cone-shaped cutting devices are mounted in such a way that they intermesh and rotate together as the bit drills. The bit body may be fitted with nozzles, or jets, through which the drilling fluid is discharged.

trip *n*: the operation of hoisting the drill stem from and returning it to the wellbore. *v*: shortened form of "make a trip."

trip in *v*: to lower the drill stem, tubing, casing, or sucker rods into the wellbore.

triplex pump *n*: a reciprocating pump with three pistons or plungers.

trip out *v*: to pull the drill stem out of the wellbore to change the bit, to change from a core barrel to the bit, to run electric logs, to prepare for a drill stem test, to run casing, and so on.

tripping *n*: the operation of hoisting the drill stem out of and returning it to the wellbore. See *make a trip*.

true-to-gauge hole *n*: a hole that is the same size as the bit that was used to drill it. It is frequently referred to as a full-gauge hole.

tubing tongs *n pl*: large wrenches used to break out and make up tubing. They may be operated manually, hydraulically, or pneumatically.

tubular goods *n pl*: any kind of pipe. Oilfield tubular goods include tubing, casing, drill pipe, and line pipe. Also called tubulars.

tungsten carbide bit *n*: a type of roller cone bit with inserts made of tungsten carbide. Also called tungsten carbide insert bit.

tungsten carbide insert bit *n*: see *tungsten carbide bit*.

U

undergauge bit *n*: a bit whose outside diameter is worn to the point at which it is smaller than it was when new. A hole drilled with an undergauge bit is said to be undergauge.

undergauge hole *n*: that portion of a borehole drilled with an undergauge bit.

underground blowout *n*: an uncontrolled flow of gas, salt water, or other fluid from one underground formation and into another formation that the wellbore has penetrated.

V

V-door *n*: an opening at floor level in a side of a derrick or mast. The V-door is opposite the drawworks and is used as an entry to bring in drill pipe, casing, and other tools from the pipe rack. The name comes from the fact that on the old standard derrick, the shape of the opening was an inverted V.

W

water-base mud *n*: a drilling mud in which the continuous phase is water. In water-base muds, any additives are dispersed in the water. Compare *oil-base mud*.

wellbore *n*: a borehole; the hole drilled by the bit. A wellbore may have casing in it or it may be open (uncased); or part of it may be cased, and part of it may be open. Also called a borehole or hole.

well control *n*: the methods used to control a kick and prevent a well from blowing out. Such techniques include, but are not limited to, keeping the borehole completely filled with drilling mud of the proper weight or density during all operations, exercising reasonable care when tripping pipe out of the hole to prevent swabbing, and keeping careful track of the amount of mud put into the hole to replace the volume of pipe removed from the hole during a trip.

wind guy line *n*: the wireline attached to ground anchors to provide lateral support for a mast or derrick. Compare *load guy line*.

wireline *n*: a small-diameter metal line used in wireline operations. Also called slick line.

wire rope *n*: a cable composed of steel wires twisted around a central core of fiber or steel wire to create a rope of great strength and considerable flexibility. Wire rope is used as drilling line (in rotary and cable-tool rigs), coring line, servicing line, winch line, and so on. It is often called cable or wireline; however, wireline is a single, slender metal rod, usually very flexible. Compare *wireline*.

Review Questions
LESSONS IN ROTARY DRILLING
Unit I, Lesson 1
The Rotary Rig and Its Components

1. Name the four major systems used on all rotary drilling rigs.

    (1) _____

    (2) _____

    (3) _____

    (4) _____

2. Which of the following is *not* a component of a power system? _____
    (1) Generator
    (2) Substructure
    (3) Prime mover
    (4) Mechanical or electric drive
    (5) Compound

3. The prime mover is the basic source of rig power.
    _____True

    _____False

4. The compound distributes power to the _____ , the_____,

    the _____ , and the _____ .

5. The hoisting system consists of the substructure, the _____or

    _____ , the drawworks, and the_____ _____ .

6. A mast usually remains a single unit after manufacture and is relatively portable.
    _____True

    _____False

7. Which of the following pieces of equipment does *not* form part of a drawworks system?

    (1) The breakout and makeup catheads

    (2) The automatic catshaft

    (3) A brake system

    (4) A transmission

    (5) A choke panel

8. The crown block always requires one more sheave than the traveling block.

    _____True

    _____False

9. What is the primary purpose of the blocks and drilling line?

    _____

    _____

    _____

    _____

10. Label the parts of the drill stem.

    • drill pipe connection

    • hexagonal kelly

    • kelly saver sub

    • lower kelly valve

    • rotary box connection RH

    • swivel sub

    • upper kelly valve

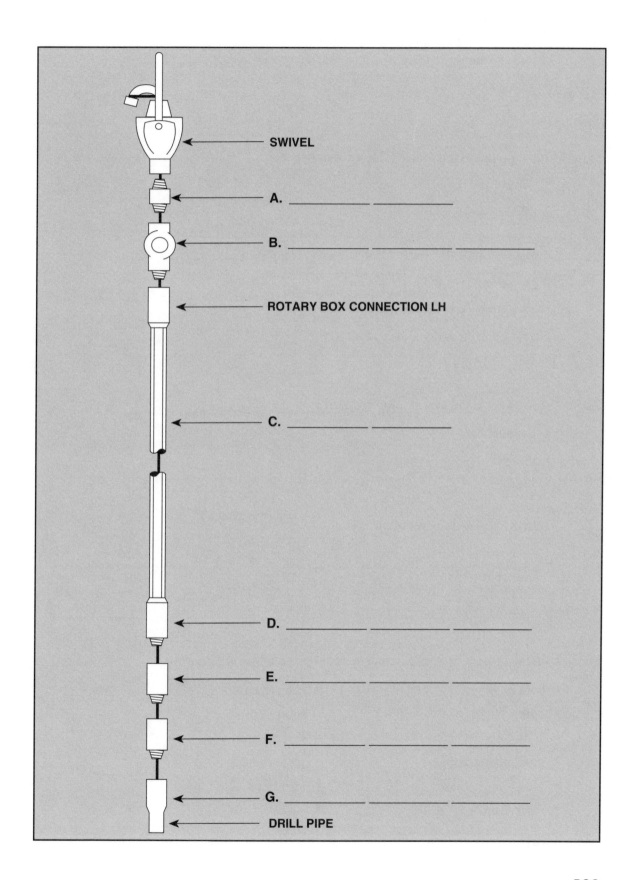

SWIVEL

A. _____ _____

B. _____ _____ _____

ROTARY BOX CONNECTION LH

C. _____ _____

D. _____ _____ _____

E. _____ _____ _____

F. _____ _____ _____

G. _____ _____ _____

DRILL PIPE

11.   The swivel rotates the kelly.

_____True

_____False

12.   With a top drive, the rotary table does not rotate.

_____True

_____False

13.   Range 2 drill pipe, the most commonly used length, is _____

(1)   18–22 feet (5.5–6.7 metres)

(2)   18–45 feet (5.5–13.7 metres)

(3)   27–30 feet (8.2–9.1 metres)

(4)   38–45 feet (11.9–13.7 metres)

14.   A three-joint stand of drill pipe is called a _____

(1)   thribble

(2)   double

(3)   fourble

15.   Name the two main types of bit:

(1)   _____

(2)   _____

16.   Label the parts of the circulating system on the following drawing.

- bulk mud bins
- dump valves
- kelly
- mud mixing hopper
- mud pump
- reserve pit

- reserve tank
- rotary hose
- shaker tank
- shale shaker
- standpipe
- suction tank

- swivel

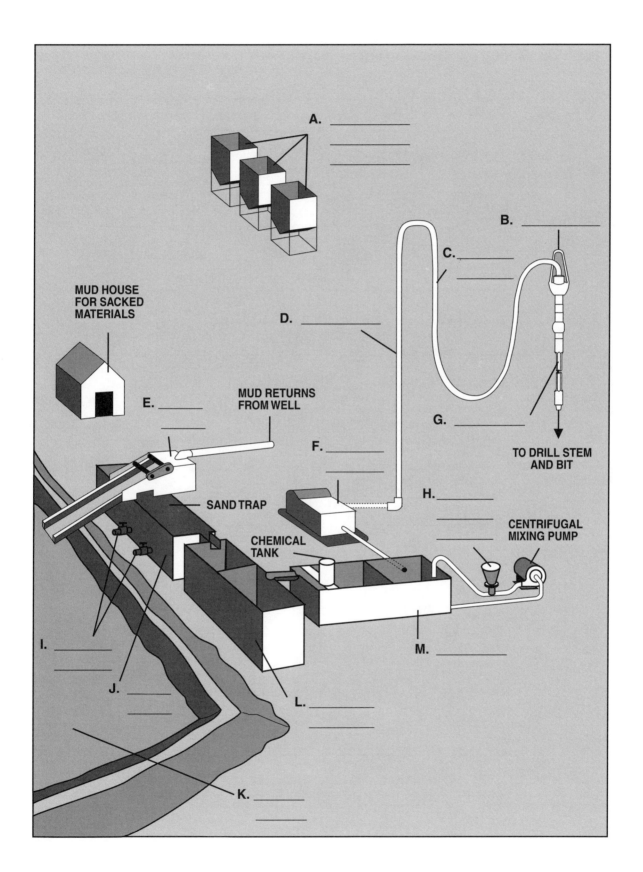

A. _____

_____

_____

B. _____

C. _____

_____

MUD HOUSE
FOR SACKED
MATERIALS

D. _____

E. _____

MUD RETURNS
FROM WELL

_____

G. _____

F. _____

_____

TO DRILL STEM
AND BIT

SAND TRAP

H. _____

_____

CENTRIFUGAL
MIXING PUMP

CHEMICAL
TANK

I. _____

_____

_____

J. _____

_____

L. _____

_____

M. _____

K. _____

_____

17.   The principal purposes of circulating fluid are to—

(1)   _____

_____

(2)   _____

_____

(3)   _____

_____

(4)   _____

_____

(5)   _____

_____

18.   Which of the following is *not* used as a drilling fluid? _____

(1)   Barite

(2)   Water

(3)   Drilling mud

(4)   Gas

(5)   Foam

19.   What do the mud pumps do?

_____

_____

_____

_____

_____

20. What causes a blowout?

    _____

    _____

    _____

    _____

21. Name the components of a typical blowout preventer stack.

    (1) _____

    _____

    (2) _____

    _____

    (3) _____

    _____

22. An annular preventer cannot close on open hole.

    _____ True

    _____ False

23. Name the five primary well-control components.

    (1) _____

    (2) _____

    (3) _____

    (4) _____

    (5) _____

24. Which of the following is *not* part of the auxiliary equipment on a rotary drilling rig? ___

    (1) Electricity generators

    (2) Mud pumps

    (3) Air compressors

    (4) Degasser

    (5) Desilter and desander

25. Name the members of a typical crew on a land rig.

    (1) _____

    (2) _____

    (3) _____

    (4) _____

    (5) _____

    (6) _____

    (7) _____

Answers to Review Questions
LESSONS IN ROTARY DRILLING
Unit I, Lesson 1
The Rotary Rig and Its Components

1. (1) the power system;
   (2) the hoisting system;
   (3) the rotating system;
   (4) the circulating system

2. (2)

3. True

4. pumps, drawworks, rotary, auxiliaries

5. derrick or mast; blocks; drilling line

6. True

7. (5)

8. True

9. To support the load of pipe in the derrick or mast as the pipe is lowered into or withdrawn from the hole

10. A. swivel sub
    B. upper kelly valve (kelly cock)
    C. hexagonal kelly
    D. rotary box connection RH
    E. lower kelly valve
    F. kelly saver sub
    G. drill pipe connection

11. False

12. True

13. (3)

14. (1)

15. (1) roller cone bits;
    (2) fixed cutter

16. A. bulk mud bins
    B. swivel
    C. rotary hose
    D. standpipe

    E. shale shaker
    F. mud pump
    G. kelly
    H. mud mixing hopper
    I. dump valves
    J. shaker tank
    K. reserve pit
    L. reserve tank
    M. suction tank

17. (1) clean the bottom of the hole;
      (2) cool and lubricate the bit and the drill stem;
      (3) flush cuttings from the hole;
      (4) support the walls of the well;
      (5) prevent the entry of formation fluid into the borehole

18. (1)

19. Circulate drilling fluid from the pit, through the drill stem, to the bit, back up the annulus, and back to the pit

20. A blowout can occur when formation pressure exceeds the pressure applied to it by the column of drilling fluid.

21. (1) annular preventer;
      (2) at least one pipe ram;
      (3) a blind ram

22. False

23. (1) drilling mud;
      (2) blowout preventers;
      (3) accumulator;
      (4) choke manifold;
      (5) mud-gas separator

24. (2)

25. (1) company representative;
      (2) toolpusher;
      (3) driller;
      (4) derrickhand;
      (5) motorhand;
      (6) mechanic;
      (7) rotary helper